JULIET ASHBY
Midnight Lover

Silhouette *Romance*
Published by Silhouette Books New York
America's Publisher of Contemporary Romance

Other Silhouette Books by Juliet Ashby

One Man Forever

SILHOUETTE BOOKS, a Division of Simon & Schuster, Inc.
1230 Avenue of the Americas, New York, N.Y. 10020

Copyright © 1983 by Juliet Ashby

Distributed by Pocket Books

ISBN: 0-671-57258-X

First Silhouette Books printing November, 1983

10 9 8 7 6 5 4 3 2 1

Map by Ray Lundgren

America's Publisher of Contemporary Romance

Printed in the U.S.A.

"I'd Like You to Do a Story on Divorce."

"I have the feeling this is something you can do very well." For the first time his eyes almost met hers. "But then you do almost everything well."

Dismissed, Kim thought. She stood up, walked past him, noting the grey suit she remembered so well. Once she'd smudged lipstick near the left lapel. The smudge was gone. Mechanically, she reached for the doorknob.

Before she realized what was happening, his big body lunged past her. He slammed the door shut and stood against it, his body a barricade.

"Come here." His eyes seemed to devour her. "Come here to me."

JULIET ASHBY
comes from a family of newspaper reporters and editors. She herself was a reporter for a metropolitan daily paper and has written for many leading women's magazines. Her hobbies are walking in London or Paris, reading and decorating.

Dear Reader:

I'd like to take this opportunity to thank you for all your support and encouragement of Silhouette Romances.

Many of you write in regularly, telling us what you like best about Silhouette, which authors are your favorites. This is a tremendous help to us as we strive to publish the best contemporary romances possible.

All the romances from Silhouette Books are for you, so enjoy this book and the many stories to come. I hope you'll continue to share your thoughts with us, and invite you to write to us at the address below:

Karen Solem
Editor-in-Chief
Silhouette Books
P.O. Box 769
New York, N.Y. 10019

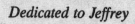
Dedicated to Jeffrey

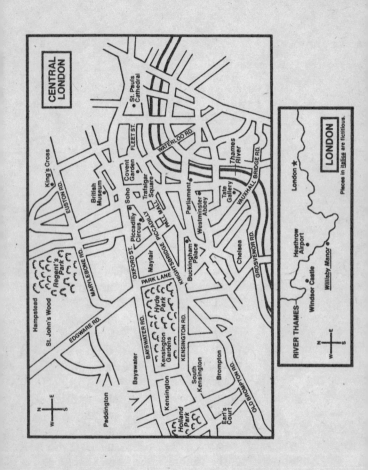

Chapter One

"Kim," Wally said around his cigar, "your turn in the boiler room. Don't let the heat get to you."

Kim Curtis looked up from her typewriter, smiled at the grizzled, homely face of her city editor and said, "Don't worry, I won't." Then she picked up a wad of copy paper and a pencil, just in case the new publisher of the *Recorder* should say something noteworthy. In all probability, though, she would be treated to more of his thinly veiled warnings. For the past two days, since taking over at his father's desk, Jon Dumont had been interviewing the *Recorder* staff—shaking everybody up, Kim thought sourly—letting them know that he was watching and evaluating, and that he was ready to go scalping.

Dumont had set the tone on his first day on the job.

7

"From now on, you're going to have to be superior newspeople," he'd told the staff, standing apprehensively around him in the newsroom. "Note I didn't say good newsmen—or even very good. I said *superior*. I expect each of you to be the kind of newsperson the *New York Times* will be trying to steal from me. Translated into simpler terms, you're going to have to start working your tails off."

Obviously flexing his muscles, Kim thought now, as she recalled that initial meeting with the big-shouldered, imposing man who bore scarcely any resemblance to his father. Edward Dumont was small, wispy, basically shy and a darling.

There was no denying though, that Jon Dumont's tough talk had accomplished what he meant it to. The usually easygoing staff was scared and scurrying. Even Dave Wharton, the top rewriteman, wore an edgy look, perhaps because he suspected the new boss wouldn't look kindly on the padded expense accounts that until now had kept the best brand of Scotch in Dave's bottom drawer.

Kim didn't pad her expense accounts; she wasn't in the least scared and she had no intention of scurrying.

Of course, she reminded herself, she didn't have as much at stake as most of the other staffers. She had no family to support, and felt sure she could always land a job on another newspaper. Not that it would ever come to that. She simply could not imagine losing her job on the *Recorder*.

Now, winding her way around newsroom desks to the publisher's office, she held her head confidently. Jon Dumont said he wanted superior staffers. She was superior. Ergo, no problem. It wasn't conceit, just the simple truth. She loved her job, performed it with enthusiasm and skill—so why feel intimidated? The fact that she had twice caught the new publisher looking at her with wary, speculative eyes didn't faze her in the least. He would soon discover that despite her appearance and three short years of experience she was equal to any reporter on the staff. Newspaper people weren't inclined to flowery phrases, but old Mr. Dumont had once publicly called Kim "my personal discovery"—and supplemented the compliment with a substantial raise.

Probably the younger Dumont was judging her by her looks, Kim thought now—misjudging her, that is. It had happened before. She realized that she looked much younger than her twenty-five years. Her slender, almost fragile build, her small, pale oval face under its cap of golden brown hair and her large sky blue eyes with their fringe of dusky lashes made her seem slightly vulnerable, if not helpless.

Jon Dumont couldn't know that it was quite often useful, looking the way she did. Tough city detectives, gazing into Kim's luminous eyes, frequently gave out more information than they had intended. Politicians tended to forget to be glib. And ordinary citizens, wary of the press, found themselves turning unaccountably confidential.

Few people realized how much steel Kim had in her makeup, how much strength she could summon when needed.

Now, reaching the threshold of Dumont's office, she paused, one hand raised to knock on the half-open door, and looked in at the man with his back turned to her.

He was gazing out the window facing busy Broad Street, four stories below. Philadelphia's traffic sent up its raucous cacaphony as Dumont shifted his weight. Kim, eyeing the broad back and shoulders and the classic shape of the man's head, saw one word flash in her mind, and that was *vitality*.

Yes, there was an alive quality about the man, an appearance of restless mobility—as if he might suddenly swerve or grasp or lunge—a look that proclaimed unbounded exuberance and vigor.

And there was something in that very air of vitality that breathed sex, Kim realized abruptly. For a flaring second she felt an unexpected warmth in her cheeks because, somewhere in the back room of her imagination, she had fantasized her own body in contact with his.

An absurd wayward thought, and one completely out of context with reality, she told herself. But still, she found herself taking a deep, steadying breath before she rapped on the open door and said, "Mr. Dumont?"

He wheeled. "Miss Curtis." His smile was cursory, a flash of white teeth. He waved her to the chair facing his desk. "Let's see, you're our junior staffer, right?"

Walking to the chair, Kim held on to her casual air, although she felt an automatic tenseness at the thought of being considered a junior anything. "I suppose I could be called that." Absentmindedly she unwound her cashmere scarf; his office was much warmer than the newsroom.

"Yes, our youngest reporter," Dumont went on, as if he hadn't heard her. She saw now that he had yesterday's paper open to her interview with Pamela Bryant, star of a new hit movie.

"Frankly," Kim said lightly, "I never think in terms of age. Just ability."

"Which is a plus for you," Dumont said quickly, and darted a sharp look at her. He had a rough-hewn, slightly off-balance face that would be easy to remember. His dark eyebrows formed a heavy bridge over penetrating hazel eyes. Looking into those eyes, Kim felt an odd sensation, as if she were pinned down.

"Now," Dumont went on, "what we'll have to work on is persuading you to think in equally free-flowing modern terms about the way you conduct interviews for this paper—with an emphasis on equal treatment of women."

"Women?" Kim frowned. "Mr. Dumont, perhaps you don't understand—I don't do Woman's Page items, I do general news."

"I'm very much aware of your function, Miss Curtis. I must add that I find the Woman's Page writers more realistic in their approach to women than our newsroom reporters seem to be."

"I'm afraid I can't agree with you, Mr. Dumont."

"Whether you agree or not is not pertinent, is it, Miss Curtis?" he said gently. "The staff of the *Recorder* will have one purpose in the days to come: To satisfy me and my conception of what this paper ought to be."

"Oh, I understand that, Mr. Dumont." Kim carefully avoided any wry emphasis.

But she knew the man opposite her was fully aware of the sardonic cast of her thoughts; his eyelids flickered revealingly. Smiling a little, he sat back in his swivel chair. "Miss Curtis, I've spent the past two months studying this paper very carefully, and I've come to the conclusion that our news and features consistently fail to reflect modern attitudes. Our writers settle too easily for weary clichés. For example"—he tapped the spread-out newspaper on his desk—"this piece you wrote yesterday."

"The city editor was satisfied, Mr. Dumont," Kim said stiffly.

"But the *publisher* found it unimaginative and imperceptive, a long exercise in stereotyping."

Kim swallowed the feeling of shock in her throat, and shifted in her chair. She managed somehow to come up with a reasonably calm voice. "I'm sure I don't *think* in stereotypes, Mr. Dumont—in fact, I very consciously try *not* to. So would you mind explaining a little further?"

"Not at all. That's why I called you in here." He thrust the newspaper in her direction. "Here, let me show you."

As she reached across the desk for the paper, his large hand collided with hers. Resenting the swift response of her pulse, Kim kept her face impassive as she stared at the paragraphs of black type.

"This was just a routine interview with a movie star," she managed finally. "What exactly is there to object to?"

Was there something like amusement in those alert hazel eyes or was she imagining it? Could he possibly have sensed the startling impact his touch had had on her?

"Miss Curtis, I haven't brought you in here just to needle you."

"I never imagined you did."

"That's precisely what you imagined. But no matter. Now understand, you've got an acceptable style—terse, yet colorful. But you have this tendency to swallow the pap the press agents hand out, and that's an out-of-date attitude. I expect my reporters to go past the surface of things, look hard at the realities. Here you've got a movie star who earns maybe a million dollars a year. Yet you expect us to believe this puffery you've written —how she spends long afternoons baking cakes and pies for her six-year-old. Actually you and I—*and* our readers—know very well that Pam Bryant couldn't tell an oven from a percolator. Every time you write stuff like this, you perpetuate a myth. You also add to the phony conceptions of women—in this case, the old chestnut that even the most successful woman is truly happy only while working over a stove. Why not tell the truth: That Pam Bryant is waited on hand and foot by five servants, that her six-year-old has about as much contact with her as I have with the planet Jupiter, and that she actually believes all children under eighteen should be hustled off to boarding school so one doesn't have to deal with them till they are fully civilized."

"But how do you know that's true?" Kim cried. "A reporter can only use the information she's given. If the woman says she likes to cook—"

"I know this isn't quite fair, Miss Curtis, but I happen to know Pam Bryant rather well." Jon Dumont smiled in a smug way that made Kim want to scratch at him. "I happen to be personally familiar with her true feelings. As you could have been if you had dug deeper and asked more penetrating questions. You could have come up with the prize, the gleaming precious metal of truth. You see, today's skilled reporter doesn't echo just what he's told. He also reports what he sees and senses. If you doubt what you've been told, you can always relate it in such a manner that the reader knows you're talking with tongue in cheek. Today's readers have no patience with fairy tales, Miss Curtis, and while I'm publishing the *Recorder* we're not going to run them. And most of the fairy tales, for some reason, seem to involve women. Suppose we start treating women the way we treat men—let them be real people. Agreed, Miss Curtis?"

He stood up, circled the desk and stopped in front of it, only a foot or so away from her. Leaning back, he crossed his arms over his chest in an attitude that instantly turned him into an adversary.

And for a moment Kim almost rose to the bait and turned openly antagonistic.

But that instinctive reaction didn't make sense, she realized. Not because she wanted to kowtow, but because what he was saying was not unreasonable.

Actually, the idea of a harder, more realistic approach to reporting appealed to her, although she had a sneaking feeling it could lead to difficulties.

"Don't you think, Mr. Dumont, that your approach might be workable with unimportant people, but a little more complicated with the bigwigs? I mean, you could say a truck driver smells sweaty, but suppose the mayor smells sweaty. Would you say that too?"

He gave her one of his sharp, deep looks. "You would if you work for me. Let me be the one to worry about complications." He smiled. "You know, the truth sometimes sounds pretty bad, but it can turn out to be the best treatment in the end. I'm reminded of a piece a little girl reporter did for me back in New York. I was an editor on *Today* magazine, as you may know. . . ."

"I know, Mr. Dumont." Kim kept her eyes lowered, so he wouldn't see the wry gleam in them. How modest of him to hint that perhaps there was someone on the *Recorder* who didn't know about his career on one of the most powerful news magazines in the country.

"Yes, well, this little girl reporter—"

"Mr. Dumont, excuse me, but aren't you indulging in some stereotyping yourself? I realize we females have been called 'little girl reporters' since the days of Nellie Bly—it's standard newspaperese—but don't you think it's time we deserved to be called women? And getting down to facts, was this reporter you're talking about really little or really a girl?"

The faintest hint of a flush mounted his cheeks. "Good for you. As a matter of fact, Sally Begner was on the tall, rangy side and had probably celebrated her fortieth birthday long ago. All right, I'll correct myself: This *woman* reporter on *Today* magazine—"

"Much better." Kim felt a spurt of warmth for him. She liked a man who could accept being bested. She also liked a man who was hard to best.

And the smile he was giving her at the moment was broader, obviously more genuine. "She did a story about a young mother who delivered quadruplets on the Fourth of July. Four kids on the Fourth—it was a natural. But instead of bringing us the standard pap about the bliss and glory of having four babies to add to the two already at home, Sally wrote a story of a young girl bowed down with the weight of too many children, no help, not much money and a deep resentment against a fate that had saddled her with more than she could bear. There wasn't a saccharine line in that story, no hearts or flowers. It was so truthful that it touched off a wave of real feeling for the woman. In fact, it grossed her about twenty thousand dollars in donations from people who sympathized—because they knew that this was the way it really was and they recognized the authentic grain of truth."

There was a long moment of silence. Then Kim nodded. "It sounds good. I'm all for that kind of approach. Of course it won't always be possible to get the whole truth. . . ."

"Some reporters manage pretty well. For example, that piece we ran the other day about the fellow in jail who got himself beaten up because he wouldn't stop singing "Anchors Aweigh," sang it day and night till he drove everybody crazy. That was a gem, that story. Very brief, hard, tough. I know it's difficult for a woman to look at things that way, but you could learn, I'm sure."

"I'm sure too," Kim said quietly, pausing a moment for effect. "I wrote that story."

For a moment he said nothing. Then his grin came—wide, startlingly open. "Bingo," he said.

After which he immediately set about reclaiming his seat of power. "So since we know you *can,* Miss Curtis"—he held her eyes for a challenging moment—"we will expect the best from you in the future. Agreed?"

His hands fell to his sides. His posture and expression indicated dismissal.

Kim started up out of her chair, and felt something at her feet. She looked down at her scarf, which had spilled from her lap.

Before she could reach for it, Jon Dumont leaned

over, presenting her with the top of his head, a thatch of lustrous dark brown hair.

When he straightened, her scarf dangled from his hand.

"Oh, thank you." Kim reached out, but he didn't surrender the scarf immediately. Instead, startlingly, he ran it through his fingers in an almost sensuous gesture. "Lovely . . . Scotland?"

She swallowed. "England." It was hard to get the word out.

He continued to hold the scarf. It looked oddly helpless; the fuzzy mauve and purple threads somehow seemed overcome, clutched by those large hands.

"I got it in London, actually," she choked out, almost snatching it from him. Avoiding his eyes, she said: "Is there anything more, Mr. Dumont?"

"Nothing more, Miss Curtis." He moved back behind his desk, his face suddenly empty of expression.

Kim hurried to the door, feeling awkward for some reason and oddly disturbed by a worn spot she had noticed on the tip of her grey suede pump.

She didn't go back to the newsroom immediately, but stood instead in the small reception room that led to the corridor. She needed to be alone for a moment. She felt as if she had been running in a marathon and had disarranged her normal metabolism. She stared down at the scarf dangling from her hand, then looped it quickly around her throat, where, for some reason, it burned against her skin.

Chapter Two

The clock was edging toward 7 P.M. Kim's working day was almost finished when Wally drifted over from the city desk. Puffing on his cigar, he eyed her curiously. He was a swarthy gnome of a man with eyes like radar.

"How did things go in there?" He nodded toward Dumont's office.

"Fine," Kim said lightly. "Just fine."

"Glad to hear it. His style takes a little getting used to, after thirty years of dealing with the old man."

"Or even after three years," Kim said.

"You really been here that long?" Wally gave her one of his rare smiles. "Say, take an obit from Phil in Malvern, will you? Some local lady who used to sing at the Academy back in the twenties. Today was one of those days when lots of people decided to die."

There was just a hint of apology in Wally's voice.

During Kim's early days on the paper, obituary assignments had been a sore point between her and the city editor.

She had joined the staff of the *Recorder* after working two college summers as a copy girl, toting coffee and clippings for reporters. She was hired on a permanent basis by Edward Dumont. Wally, not too happy about being handed a novice when what he really needed was a skilled police reporter, decided to test Kim's stamina by serving her a steady diet of obits. The funeral assignment—hours of writing about death—almost dampened her joy at having at last become a full-fledged newswoman.

For over a month she sat grimly lashed to obits. And then, on one dour day—a grey pelting rain didn't help her mood at all—she arrived at the newsroom, took a look at the piled-up death notices atop her typewriter and eyed the other woman reporter who was happily heading out to cover a juicy custody trial. Kim then marched herself to the city desk and announced to Wally that henceforth she was going to report to work dressed entirely in black. She hoped it wouldn't depress or unsettle the staff.

"I might even be able to root out a raven or two to sit on my shoulder," she declared fiercely.

"You'll look okay in black," Wally rejoined stonily around his cigar.

But later that day he sent her out on her first real assignment, interviewing a retiring circus queen.

The next morning Kim opened the *Recorder* in delirious triumph. There it was on page 3: "Circus Queen Says Big Top Doomed." And under that heading, the magic words: By Kim Curtis.

After that she and Wally were fast friends. And only occasionally was she assigned the dreary job of handling death notices.

Now, deftly dispatching the one at hand, she glanced at the clock and plopped the cover on her typewriter. As far as news was concerned, it had been a dull day, but something lively seemed to be going on behind her, judging by Hal Thurmond's booming laugh.

"What's so funny?" She turned to look at Thurmond, who sat with his chair tilted back.

The redheaded reporter grinned and passed her a glossy photo. "The new boss resting on his dignity, minus the pinstripes and the two-hundred-dollar shoes."

Kim looked at the photo. Jon Dumont, in ski clothes, lay prone in the snow. Alongside him, one of her skis in sharp alignment with his head, lay a young woman, who looked glamorous even in this grainy, slightly blurred action photo.

Someone had obviously dug it up out of the files and was now passing it around the newsroom. The photo was dated two years back. The caption read: "Gallantry on the Slopes. What a way to go! proclaims Jon Dumont, a *Today* magazine editor. Dumont displays a gallant smile on the Aspen slopes despite his painful encounter with a wayward ski worn by blond New York model Jeannie Begley. The two are a current item around New York nite spots."

Kim stared in fascination at the photo. That small V-shaped scar she'd noticed on Dumont's forehead—was that his souvenir of Aspen? She looked from Dumont to the girl lying beside him in the snow bank.

She'd seen that face before, promoting skin creams and lipstick.

Suddenly she realized she was clutching the glossy too tightly, actually wrinkling it. Forcing her fingers to relax, she smoothed the photograph, puzzling over her reaction to this man. It was bizarre, absurd, as if she had never before encountered a sexually appealing male.

Which Dumont was, there was no denying that. Even in this undignified photo, the sight of him stirred her physically, made her feel a stab of envy for the girl who had had the luck to tumble in the snow with him. Of course he would do well with women. Women young or old would eat him up. Smiling that smug smile, he had said that he happened to know Pam Bryant rather well. Oh well, Kim consoled herself, some men made a point of being seen with models and movie actresses. Just as some brainless women made a point of being seen with power symbols like Jon Dumont.

Without comment she dropped the glossy print back on Thurmond's desk, grabbed up her trenchcoat and shoulder bag and hurried out. Usually she hated the working day to end, but tonight she felt oddly unsettled, wanting something and not quite sure what. But of course she had been working very hard, she reminded herself. She hadn't had dinner out, or seen a movie or had a date for . . . could it possibly be four whole weeks?

She was passing the reception room when the sound of Cookie's voice caught up with her. "Kim, come on in!" Cookie called. "I've been trying to get a minute with you all day!"

Kim ducked into the tiny room where, for quite a number of years, Emma Cooke—Cookie to everyone on the paper—had presided as secretary-receptionist and devoted protector of Edward Dumont. She was probably in her early sixties, but it was hard to remember, particularly when she smiled. A wide space between her two front teeth lent her a hoydenish Halloween air—a startling contrast to her marshmallow white hair and finely wrinkled skin.

"I brought you a present. Remember you said you need a flowering plant for your window?" Cookie took a flowerpot from the small forest lining her windowsill. "These slips are from my prize begonia, the loveliest, fullest plant I've ever had."

"Oh, Cookie, you're a dream. Thanks so much."

"Put them in your sunniest spot. Not too much water, now." Cookie deftly wound a cone of newsprint around the flowerpot. And then suddenly the older woman's hands froze; a grimace of pain tightened the delicate skin around her eyes.

"Cookie!" Kim took a worried step toward her. "What's the matter?"

"Nothing . . . nothing. Touch of rheumatism, just a twinge." Cookie's voice was breathless, but she gave her wide smile. "Comes with growing ancient. Nothing you would know anything about."

"That's silly, you're younger than anyone I know." Kim patted the secretary's shoulder. Then, out of the corner of her eye, she became aware of the moving silhouette behind the frosted glass panels separating Cookie's office from Dumont's. She felt her breath quicken. "Come on," she said quickly. "I'll walk you to the bus."

"That's right, it is time to go, isn't it?" Cookie shook her head. "I've been so busy I haven't noticed. It's wild in here these days."

The older woman scooped up her things and together they went out to the corridor, Kim feeling a flicker of annoyance at her own too-rapid movements, the irrational feeling that she needed to escape. It wasn't like her to run from anyone.

But of course she hadn't combed her hair or freshened her makeup. Maybe that was why she didn't want to come in contact with Dumont. After all, it was natural to want to look fairly presentable around a new employer.

Except she knew that wasn't the whole of it. The truth was, she didn't feel up to being around the man again. She needed time to sort out her feelings. Jon Dumont made her feel jittery. And the jitters were utterly unlike her. She prided herself on being emotionally sturdy, in command of herself. Even at the height of her romance with Alan Skilton, she had been in control, completely self-possessed. In fact, that had probably been the main factor behind her decision to return Alan's engagement ring. She couldn't shake the sense of incompleteness, the feeling that if she married Alan she would some day wake up and realize she had settled for something that wasn't quite *it,* wasn't quite the big barnfire, the sizzle and scorch and blaze of genuine love.

"There's the elevator!" Cookie said, and the two of them worked themselves into the crowd just as the doors started to close.

"Hold it!"

The voice zooming down the corridor made Cookie

jump. "It's Mr. Dumont," she said in a flustered voice as she stabbed nervously at the button that kept the doors open.

"Thank you, ladies." Jon Dumont, taking long easy strides, wedged himself into the cage, his shoulder nudging hard against Kim's. She gave him an indignant glance. Why couldn't he have waited for the next car? He was making everyone uncomfortable with his big, imposing frame. His thigh was practically welded to hers, and if he took a step backward he would probably annihilate the tiny woman behind him.

Kim realized suddenly that he was looking at her and that he had seen her resentment. He gave his slashing white grin. "Sorry to crowd you, Miss Curtis."

His eyes had a bold look. They held hers just a moment too long to be casual. Struggling to edge away from him, although there was no place to go, Kim wondered if she were imagining the challenge in his eyes—a man-woman kind of challenge.

"I'm not worried about *me*," she said in a high voice that sounded terribly unnatural. "But please have mercy on my plant." She indicated the frail begonia slips, crushed against her chest.

"No problem."

Before she realized what was happening, he had taken the flowerpot out of her hands. He hoisted it up, and held it far over the heads of the other passengers.

"That's right, Kim, crack that old whip—put the boss to work!"

Kim recognized the voice coming over her shoulder. It belonged to Doug Norman, from the copy desk. Some people laughed. Others glanced warily at Dumont, wondering how he would take to such familiarity. They know he's different from the old man, Kim thought. They're all afraid of him.

She was too. She wanted to deny it; she hated the whole idea of being afraid of anybody. But the truth was that the sensations she felt from this man's body nudging hers were not unconnected with fear of herself, of her own startlingly vivid reaction to him. Or was she letting her imagination go berserk? she wondered, when the elevator doors opened on the lobby and a very matter-of-fact Jon Dumont handed her the flowerpot.

"Thank you, very nice of you," she babbled, trying to give the impression of someone who, though polite, was much too busy to dally.

But he didn't answer, didn't even seem to hear her. He just gave a nod and turned away so quickly that it was obvious he had no time to dally, either.

Feeling ridiculously annoyed, Kim hurried through the revolving doors, hoping to catch up with Cookie and invite her to dinner. But Cookie must have gotten lucky and caught her bus just as it pulled up, for she was nowhere in sight.

Poor Cookie, Kim thought. It must be rough, outliving a husband by a quarter of a century and each night going home to an empty house, a house she had once come to as a glowing bride.

Stepping into the windy October evening, Kim found herself remembering Alan Skilton's words: "You know what the trouble is in living alone? You get used to it. You get used to eating by yourself, talking to yourself, sleeping with yourself. You could make it a habit and grow old that way, old and lonely."

Kim realized the memory had followed naturally on

the heels of her contemplation of Cookie's lonely state. And now that she thought about it, maybe Alan was right. She had turned down his offer of marriage, and after that she had turned down his request to move in with him. And now maybe she was growing too comfortable with just herself. After all, it had been four whole weeks since she'd had a date. That fact might explain her overreaction to Dumont.

She remembered how much she had enjoyed Alan's companionship, the cartoons he had clipped and saved for her, the way they had gotten excited about the same recording stars. There was no doubt that having a male friend around added a lovely spice to life. And at the moment even the most mild romance seemed better than no romance at all.

Abruptly, she became aware of the wind whistling through her unlined trenchcoat, and the darkening sky looked somehow vastly depressing. She ran to the curb and waved down a cab.

Home was a small circle of golden warmth, a Society Hill apartment with a fascinating view of houses dating back to Revolutionary days. Kim stood in her yellow kitchen heating chili to pile atop a taco shell. After that she mixed an enormous green salad. As she worked, she found herself comparing Alan Skilton with Jon Dumont, much to Alan's disadvantage. She had seen Dumont only three times, and very briefly, but it was surprising how clearly she remembered the texture of his tanned skin, the glossy richness of his hair, the precise shape of the scar that had probably been donated by his glamorous skiing companion. He had such a big body, yet he was so quick moving, obviously an athlete. For a moment she imagined him undressed. He would be a sculptor's dream, like that marvelous statue in the Rodin museum on the Parkway.

Alan had an acute aversion to athletics. He even made stale jokes about it. "Whenever I feel like exercising, I just go lie down till the feeling passes away."

She smiled, remembering. Remembering too that for a while she had almost believed she was in love with Alan. She had, in fact, actually accepted his engagement ring. Although Alan had a wonderful sense of humor, particularly if the joke wasn't on him, and a tremendous awareness of the sensual pleasures—he insisted on good food, good music and good company —she had come to realize an intangible important something was lacking. He charmed, but didn't hold her. He could go out of town on business and she would feel perfectly happy. Such detachment wouldn't be possible if she were truly in love, she decided. Eventually she took a deep breath and told Alan of her decision.

Yet sometimes as she listened to the stereo Alan had lent her and had never come around to reclaim, she found herself regretting their breakup. Perhaps she had been unrealistic, expecting him to live up to an idea of perfection no man could attain.

As for her present mood of discontent, how much of it was actually missing Alan, and how much simply emotional hunger for some unknown someone?

She began to pot Cookie's slips in blue containers that matched her sofa pillows. Would there be any staff changes now that Dumont had taken over the paper?

she wondered. Apparently he was going to give much more attention to the details of editorial policy than his father had.

Recalling his criticsm of her Pamela Bryant interview, she felt a flutter of uncertainty. Suppose she couldn't please him, couldn't hit on precisely the approach he wanted? There was a certain steeliness in him, an intractable look about his mouth. But of course a man had to give that impression when he was taking over a business. Any sign of uncertainty would be interpreted as weakness by the sharp-eyed newsmen who were already on the lookout for flaws in "Daddy's boy." Kim had heard all the kidding, all the talk about how running a newspaper with four editions a day was a far cry from working at the leisurely pace of a monthly magazine. The kidders managed to overlook the fact that on *Today* magazine Dumont had turned out a series of in-depth, behind-the-scenes articles that were many notches above the typical newspaper piece.

If she lost her job, she would have to leave this place, Kim told herself, looking around her apartment and realizing how much it meant to her. It had the most comforting look about it—soft, warm, glowing. She had bought only furnishings that would last, things so lovely she wouldn't mind the dull dusting and waxing chores. She had a real grandfather's clock in the corner, and a fine cherry bookcase next to the fireplace. She even had an authentic oriental rug—only a patch, but a very handsome patch, and almost paid for.

She had earned it all with her talents, and of course she would never have to give it up.

Growing too comfortable with yourself?

Alan's words were nudging her again. Kim arranged

the repotted slips on the window ledge and walked aimlessly around the room, angry at feeling vaguely dissatisfied instead of cosily snug and relaxed.

Abruptly she found herself at the telephone. She hesitated for a moment, then dialed Alan's number.

"Hello," he said. "This is Alan Skilton." His voice oddly slow and precise, he went on, "Sorry I'm out. If you leave your name and number, I'll be happy to get back to you, particularly if you're the stunning blonde, brunette or redhead I saw last night in the Bellevue bar."

Kim grinned. It was just like Alan to have an answering machine. He had always loved all kinds of gadgetry. And the message was like him too. He tried so hard to give the impression that he joked and breezed through life.

Except that she had come to know quite another Alan. The thought of that other Alan made her hesitate for a moment. But then, looking around the silent apartment, she decided to take the plunge. "Just saying 'Hi, how are you, Alan,'" she said into the phone, and hung up.

There. That was nebulous and casual enough. If Alan wanted to call her back, he could. If he didn't want to—if by now he was anchored to another girl—he would feel no obligation.

She stood looking around, still at loose ends, a novel feeling for her. She was rarely bored, but tonight the thought of reading or letter writing or watching TV seemed terribly uninviting.

Idly she flicked the pages of the telephone directory, and then suddenly, whimsically, turned to the Ds.

Dumont, Francine . . . Dumont, Honaire . . . Dumont, Jon.

Something stirred and rippled in her chest. She found herself remembering the look of his strong, square hands. He didn't wear rings. She liked that. She had always believed men's hands didn't need decoration. They were beautiful in themselves, looking so capable.

She bent over the directory, her cheeks abruptly hot, reading Dumont, Jon, Walnut Towers.

The Walnut Towers was a new, sleek building of condominiums going up forever into the sky, with some kind of starlike design on the roof that sent forth a golden glow at night. It was currently the chic place to live in Philadelphia, right on the edge of historic Rittenhouse Square.

What would Dumont's apartment look like? It would probably be ultra-modern, with Scandinavian furniture, Man Ray prints and mobiles waiting to snag your hair.

And on this windy purple night what was he doing? Entertaining some ravishing creature, mixing her pre-dinner drinks, nuzzling the back of her soft white neck?

Idiot, Kim said vehemently, and slammed the phone book shut. She stood for a long moment, tapping her foot. Then she dialed Megan's number.

"Got the energy to run for an hour?" she said breathlessly.

To her relief, Megan said yes.

Chapter Three

"Hey, Pete, better dig yourself up some new rags," Hal Thurmond was saying as Kim walked into the newsroom a few days later. A small band of reporters and rewritemen had clustered around the bulletin board.

"I refuse to surrender. I will appear precisely as you now see me: pure, natural and immaculate." Proudly, Pete Bailey indicated his familiar, soft worn jeans. "I wore these to interview the vice-president of the United States; they ought to do fine in Walnut Towers."

"What's happening in Walnut Towers?" Kim said casually, although for a moment the sound of the name had caused her pulse to take a startling leap.

"We're all invited to a taste of high life." Pete tapped a pink notice tacked to the bulletin board. "Food and libations in honor of the old man."

"Imagine, all of us *superior* newsmen under one

roof." Thurmond gave a mocking smile. "By the way, anyone get a bid from the *New York Times* yet? I've been waiting all week for their call."

There was a spatter of slightly uneasy laughter.

Kim gave her attention to the notice on the bulletin board:

"All members of the editorial staff are invited to attend a reception and buffet at my home, Walnut Towers (penthouse floor), on October 16 at 7 P.M. The occasion will mark my father's official retirement. We will also be wishing him *bon voyage* as he sets out on his long-awaited trip around the world. Since his closest ties have been with the people who produce this newspaper, I am hoping each of you will be able to attend. Those few on night shift may wish to work out some system with the day shift. If you spell one another, everyone will be able to spend at least some time in helping toast my father's happy future."

Dumont had signed his initials in square black letters.

"Mmm . . . should be a fun time." Carol Prince, who edited the Woman's Page, drew up alongside Kim. She was a glittery kind of woman in her forties who always wore a turban. "It's a gorgeous place, that new condo. Jan and Phil Evans had an apartment there until they split up."

"Split up?" Kim said incredulously. The Evanses were an attractive couple she had met at one of Carol's parties.

"Don't look so stunned, darling, it's the lastest news." Carol tapped cigarette ash on the floor. "But what am I doing standing here chatting? I've got to get myself a photographer. I'm doing a piece on the new boots. Rhinestones all over them. They're loathsome, but absolutely the rage for evening."

Settling at her typewriter, Kim puzzled about the Evanses. She had thought they were so much in love, a model couple. Her appraisal had apparently been dead wrong. She hated to think that she was still taken in by appearances. She should know better by now. As a reporter she had personally interviewed a baby-faced youth who had murdered two women; a clumsy, thick-fingered man who looked like a butcher and played the violin like an angel; and a sweet, big-eyed young woman arrested for gross mistreatment of her ten-month-old.

"Kim." It was Wally, calling from the city desk. "Don't take your coat off."

Grabbing up a wad of copy paper, Kim started to cross the room just as Jon Dumont appeared in the doorway. He paused, surveying the newsroom, and Kim was startled at the abrupt fierce hammering of her heart. Without looking directly at him, she was aware of everything about him—the turn of his head, the movement of his eyes, the color of his shirt and tie.

And now she felt he was looking at her. She flushed and forced herself to raise her eyes and meet the look head-on.

His lips twitched, and made the faintest sign of recognition.

The rush of excitement she felt was so insane, she was almost lightheaded from it. And nothing could be more ridiculous. The man probably went in for high-style women, and there was nothing about her that was dramatic or individual. In fact, if she were really clever, she would develop something, some kind of stylish gimmick that would set her apart. Like Carol Prince's· turbans. Or maybe she could always dress in just one color, like hot pink or purple, make it her signature.

She laughed aloud at the ludicrous image. But she was conscious of a feeling that was new to her: envy. Girls who were really striking, tall, gilt-haired girls who looked blank yet immensely desirable never rated thin, underdeveloped smiles.

At the city desk Wally looked up from his assignment sheet. "You got a cold? You look flushed."

"Oh, it's the wind. It's terrible for October."

"Yeah . . . must make it tough if you have to live in a tent."

"A tent?"

"Apparently we've got a family in the Northeast doing just that—living in a tent on a vacant lot. Two adults, three kids, one of them in diapers. Somebody phoned in the tip. Suppose you run up there and check it out. I'll send a photographer with you. Could be a real heart-wrencher."

"Right." Kim looked at the address Wally had handed her. It was far up in the Northeast, so it would be a long trip.

She hurried up to the fifth floor to pick up the photographer, relieved not to encounter Dumont in the corridor. She didn't want to run into him right now. She needed a calm, clear mind when she set out on a story.

Almost four hours later she was back in the newsroom, tired, cold and hungry, yet eager to get to her typewriter. A copy boy brought her a container of coffee and a package of peanuts, which would have to serve as her midday meal. Hunched over her machine, she typed out the pitiful tale of unemployed invalid Gus Filo and his little family. As she worked, she was scarcely conscious of the smoke and noise of the newsroom. Recreating what she had seen, struggling to give the readers the color and feel and heart of a story, was always absorbing. In this case the story dealt with loss and misfortune, poverty and fear, and Kim found herself moved by what she was writing about.

By the time she had reread her story and typed in corrections and changes, she was limp and bleary-eyed. But she didn't move from her seat until Wally had read her copy. She didn't know why she always sat surreptitiously eyeing Wally's face as he read. She knew it was useless; her city editor was the most enigmatic of men. You couldn't tell a thing from his expression. The only way you could know if your work passed muster was when you saw it in print the following day.

But today Wally broke with precedent. From across the newsroom she caught his low, wonderful growl. "Nice job, Kim. You get good pictures?"

"Yes, great," she called.

And then, because his compliment had upped her adrenaline, she reached for her dull Sunday feature on housing and spun it out quickly, tagging on just the right final sentence. Drawing a long, weary breath, she took a few minutes to repair her makeup. In the mirror her eyes had the shine of success. Maybe she wasn't high fashion, but at least she looked alive, she told herself, adding an extra dab of lipstick.

She was glad she had taken care of her appearance a few minutes later when Cookie edged into the newsroom. "There's a man outside to see you," Cookie whispered. "I didn't know if you were on deadline, so I made him wait till I saw you weren't typing. His name is Mr. Skilton."

"Oh, Alan! Thanks, Cookie." Smiling, Kim followed the secretary to the reception room, faintly surprised that Alan would come to her office. He had never done that before.

He jumped up eagerly when he saw her, his smile as warm as ever. "Hope you don't mind my coming up here." He took her arm. "I just caught up with your phone message. Since I have to be in Chicago tonight, I thought if I hurried I might be in luck and persuade you to have dinner with me before I leave." His pale grey eyes moved approvingly over her face and down to her plum wool suit and lavender blouse. "You're looking wonderful, darling."

"Thanks. You too." Alan was a handsome dresser. His narrow face was made for ascots and at the moment he was wearing a smart rust and black one, a striking contrast to his white gold hair. He was a computer salesman, and carefully cultivated the country gentleman manner, as if intimating that his wares were the aristocracy of office equipment and naturally complemented people who rode to hounds and spent weekends at the country club. It was an approach that worked. Alan was wearing a very splendid new gold Rolex, Kim noticed.

"I've got a few last-minute things to do, Alan," she said. "Can you wait fifteen minutes? Technically, I should stay another half-hour, but since I've finished my masterpiece for the day. . . ." She smiled again. There was no denying that she was glad to see him, and felt warmed by the appreciation in his eyes.

"I've been waiting for six months. Guess I can manage another fifteen minutes." Alan moved a little closer to her; Cookie had left her alcove and they were alone.

"Oh, Alan, I didn't mean . . ." Kim began, then closed her lips. This wasn't the place to go into the fact that she hadn't changed her mind since refusing to enter into any close relationship with him. Oh, dear, he thinks I have, she thought, as Alan leaned closer, pressing his lips against hers in a quick kiss.

"It's been too long, baby," he murmured huskily.

Kim glanced nervously at the door leading to Dumont's office. It was slightly ajar.

Suddenly she very much regretted the impulse that had led her to phone Alan. Over dinner he would again be urging her to move in with him, with or without a wedding ring, whichever suited her, and she would be painfully resisting. They would travel over the same old bumpy terrain.

Pushing lightly at his chest, she made a laugh. "Hey—I don't usually give at the office!"

Even as she said it, she was aware of some movement in Dumont's office . . . a creaking sound. Or was it just the wind rushing up Broad Street?

"Go," she said to Alan. "Wait in the lobby. Okay?"

"I'd say okay to anything at this moment." Alan's eyes clung to her face. "God, it's good to see you again!"

How would he have reacted if he had seen her a half-hour ago, Kim thought, with her hair windblown and her nose red? Superficial things meant so much to Alan. Too much, she thought, as she watched him walk to the elevator. Still, it was good to be admired by a man, to feel that special warming glow.

"Are we failing to supply you with enough work to occupy your time, Miss Curtis?"

With a lurch of her heart, she whirled to see Jon Dumont eyeing her from the doorway of his office.

He was joking, of course, she thought, and tried to make her smile quick and light. "Oh, I've turned out my full quota of immortal words for today, Mr. Dumont."

"You wind down rather early, by my calculation."

She looked confusedly at him. Was it some kind of joke? No one in the office felt obliged to stay riveted to a desk for every minute of the working day. Newswriters were free to take a break, to wander, chat, read rival newspapers, do anything they wanted at times when they weren't involved in a story. In fact, they needed that kind of atmosphere because once they were involved with an assignment, the work was so intense—so emotionally draining when it was poised so often on the edge of deadlines.

But Dumont knew all of that. So what could he be talking about? Certainly he wasn't objecting to her leaving a little early?

Well, whatever was bugging him, she thought, she certainly wasn't going to let herself be flustered by it.

Looking at her watch in a deliberately stagy manner, she exclaimed, "Oh, I see I *do* have a few more minutes I could use to advantage! What would you suggest, Mr. Dumont? Should I study Roget's *Thesaurus* or memorize the names of the Pulitizer Prize winners since 1918?"

She had hoped to see his smile, but he continued to eye her stonily. "Sometime when you are not in such a hurry, Miss Curtis, I'll take you aside and go into some of the difficulties this paper is facing. Since time is money, we're all going to have to start hoarding our minutes—if we want to stay in business, that is."

He started to turn away, then suddenly swung back to her. His eyes dove at her, harsh yet mesmerizing. "By the way, you ought to button up your blouse." And then he was striding back to his office, closing the door firmly behind him.

Staring after him with disbelieving eyes, Kim's face was blazing. She felt stunned, personally assaulted. She looked down at the V of her lavender shirt. Her fingers fumbled with the second open button. Then her lips tightened and she snatched her hand away. Everyone wore a shirt that way. What right had he to talk about the way she dressed?

And the way he had stared at her, those eyes going down so deep, as if wanting to search out all the parts of her. She'd had the weird feeling he was going to reach out, and savagely yank her to him.

This sort of speculation was crazy, she told herself, when it was obvious the man's only feeling about her was unremittingly hostile. Every encounter with him had involved a criticism, a complaint or an implied threat.

She was barely conscious of Cookie coming back into the room, a fat manila folder pressed to her bosom. "Whew! What a day!" Cookie rubbed at eyes that looked strained and red-rimmed. "I can't seem to catch up. This place just isn't the same anymore!"

"It certainly isn't," Kim said grimly.

As she turned to go back to the newsroom, her eyes fell on the frosted glass that separated Dumont's office from the reception room. She frowned as she saw the tall shadow passing back and forth.

Was he really that worried? she thought, suddenly remembering that he had said the paper was in financial trouble.

All at once an idea bloomed in Kim's mind. She'd noticed that a number of out-of-town newspapers, in an effort to build up their readership, were conducting contests in which alluring prizes were offered. Maybe she ought to go into Dumont's office and make the suggestion to him. *Hey, that's something I hadn't considered,* he would say, his eyes turning warm and appreciative. *Let's go to dinner and talk it over.*

She caught herself, her cheeks warming. She was being ridiculous, completely unrealistic. Jon Dumont undoubtedly knew all about circulation builders. Maybe he was already planning a contest. Or maybe he'd considered the idea and discarded it as not worthy of the *Recorder.* At any rate, she certainly wasn't going to go rushing into his office about anything. He was sure to think she was trying to ingratiate herself with him.

She bit her lip. Something about this man was sending her off her rocker. Now that she thought about it, she didn't believe for a moment that the paper was in dire straits. So they had lost a little advertising. That couldn't be disastrous. The truth was, this was just Dumont asserting himself, wanting people like poor

Cookie moored to her desk far past quitting time, to be impressed and awed by him.

Kim made sure the clock was precisely at seven before she headed for the elevator. She very deliberately didn't close her coat so that if she bumped into Dumont he would see that her shirt buttons were where she wanted them to be.

She was disappointed when there was no sign of him in the corridor. He was a man who needed a strong comeuppance. And one of these days she was going to give it to him.

"Seems awful to be taking off just as we're getting together again," Alan said as the waitress cleared away their coffee cups. "And awful to drag you all the way out here, but I've learned it's risky not to get to airports early." He reached across the table and took Kim's hand. It was the first intimate move he'd made since they had arrived at the airport. They had eaten steak sandwiches while watching the jets sweep down onto the brightly lighted field, and Kim had been relieved that the conversation was light and easy. But now that Alan's departure time was fast approaching, his knee was pressing against hers and his eyes had the shiny, desirous look she remembered.

"It's been rotten without you," he said in a low voice. "And by the way, I am now the owner of a new, king-sized bed. The man called it the Honeymoon Special, and I couldn't help hoping. . . ."

Kim felt her cheeks burning. "Alan, look, when I phoned you, I didn't mean . . . I haven't changed my mind about anything."

"Sure you have." Under the table his knee pressed closer. "Kim, you remember the super times we had, all those great dinners in Bucks County? How we always agreed on what shows to see? And did we ever run out of things to talk about? We never should have split up."

"Alan, we *did* have a good time, and I'll always be your friend. But as I've said before I can't be any more than that. I'm really sorry." She tried to convince him with her eyes. "Oh, and by the way, I've still got your stereo. When you're back in Philly, why don't you pick it up? And when you do, leave me my extra key, okay?"

"I don't give a damn about the stereo," he said sulkily. "I just can't understand why we can't be together. I've missed you so much. It's always on my mind, like a toothache."

"I don't know if I like that comparison." Kim smiled, but then realized it wasn't fair to make even a pale joke about something Alan was taking so seriously. But how could she tell him what she had gradually come to realize—that there were things in his character that bothered her, things she couldn't really admire. She had realized that he was basically a shallow man one day when he lost out on a sale. He had come apart, lost all his gloss and jauntiness, turned snappish, petty and even a little mean.

It had shocked her, and made her sense that any man she would want to be permanently involved with would have to be as sturdy as she was, certainly sturdy enough to bear the blows of life with some semblance of grace.

And she had to keep that thought in mind now, although it was titillating to be once more with a handsome, attentive man, a man whose eyes clung to hers, flashing compliments and desire.

Sometimes she wished she were more capable of self-deception. But whenever she was tempted to ignore what her brain told her was the cold truth, she remembered her scientist father's advice: "Be honest with yourself even when it hurts, even when it's agonizing. It's the only way to come to grips with life."

It hadn't been exactly agonizing to face up to the truth about Alan, but it hadn't been fun, either, Kim thought. It would be much easier right now to tell him that she wanted to try again, but she couldn't do it—particularly not now.

The unexpected realization brought her up short and became another truth she had to face a half-hour later, after she had waved goodbye to a rueful-looking Alan. *Particularly not now*. What did she mean?

But of course she knew. Jon Dumont was filling her thoughts. He was vivid, intriguing, infuriating and compelling.

This is ridiculous. I don't know anything about him, she scolded herself. But as the taxi whisked her home, she kept seeing Dumont's face—the tilting, expressive eyebrows; the flare of the long, firm lips; the powerful look of his body; those square, strong hands.

The truth was Dumont hadn't been out of her mind since their first meeting. The thought that he might sometime touch her made her heart skip a beat.

She was right to have resisted Alan. It wouldn't be fair to take up with one man—and be obsessed with another. Right now, she was totally obsessed.

Chapter Four

The next day started on a note of triumph for Kim. Her story about the Filo family, forced to live in a tent, was spread impressively over three columns on the front page. Wally hadn't cut a word, and although Kim knew every line by heart, a rereading over her breakfast coffee left her as choked up as if she had never heard of the Filos. When you reacted that way to your own story, the readers were sure to follow suit. Kim suspected that Philadelphia, which prided itself on being the City of Brotherly Love, would soon be turning its pockets inside out, opening its heart to the weary father who hungered for work but was too ill to look for it, his frail wife and the three children who had few clothes, inadequate food and a windy tent to call home.

It was wonderful to know that something you wrote could actually help alter destinies, Kim reflected, as she left her apartment an hour earlier than usual. The brisk sunny day underscored her exultant feeling. A mild celebration was certainly in order, she thought, heading for Chestnut Street and some window shopping. One of the advantages to working offbeat hours was that she could browse peacefully in uncrowded shops and buy things without waiting. It gave her a feeling of living in a special world, not having to report for work until 11 A.M.

Her favorite Chestnut Street store had a stunning window display of cocktail dresses, lush confections trimmed with beads and bands of milk-pale fur. Gazing in, Kim realized that she needed something special for Friday's party for Edward Dumont. Bailey's blue jeans notwithstanding, people were bound to dress up for an affair at the Walnut Towers penthouse.

And of course she would want to look especially nice in honor of the elder Dumont. Like everyone else on the paper, she was very fond of him; in fact, he was the one who had given her her start.

She smiled, remembering how she had written a letter to the *Recorder* when she was still in college. She'd told of her love of journalism and her determination to become a reporter. Edward Dumont had replied: "You say you're willing to tote coffee and run copy and do all the grubby parts of the news business, so I'm starting you as a copy girl the last week in June. Mind you, this doesn't guarantee you'll ever be a reporter. It's just a half-step up a long, grueling ladder."

But she'd made it to the top, thanks to Edward Dumont's kindness and encouragement. Yes, Kim told herself, she would certainly have to buy something splendid to wear in honor of that sweet, serious, thoughtful man.

And then, raising her eyes to her reflection in the shop window, she thought, Come on—it's not just Papa you're dressing for.

So all right, she wanted to impress Jon Dumont. She was feeling a passing fascination. Once she actually got to know the man, he'd probably lose his appeal. But since, for some reason, he seemed to be thrusting himself into her thoughts, why fight it? Why not let her impulses take wing—what did she have to lose?

She bought the mimosa chiffon, the one that made her waist look like a whisper. Bands of beaded chiffon crossed under a Grecian-type bodice. She bought the bronze slippers displayed with the dress, and the extravagant beaded evening bag.

Over the dressing room transom she heard two shoppers talking. "Imagine, a nine-month-old baby living in a tent! I told Bob about it at breakfast. He said write them a check. I mean, we wanted to do *something*."

Listening, Kim felt an almost irrestible urge to call out, "That was *my* story. Thanks for reading it!"

Like a naive cub reporter, she derided herself. But she knew even Dave Wharton, the paper's prize writer, got a special glow from seeing his stuff in print. She'd watched him hurriedly thumbing through the early edition, making sure not a single paragraph of his had been cut or altered. Being a reporter was like being an actor: In a way, you and your work were one and the same.

"Hi," she called to Wally when she came into the city room a half-hour later. She wasn't surprised when

Wally didn't answer. He'd given her a compliment yesterday, and he probably figured any more effusion would spoil her.

She was settling at her typewriter when Jon Dumont appeared in the doorway. He was in his shirt sleeves and his usually well-brushed hair was slightly mussed. His eyes went directly to her.

"Got a minute, Miss Curtis?"

She looked from him to Wally, expecting Wally's nod to show he knew where she was going. But Wally didn't look up from his desk. In fact, he seemed to be deliberately avoiding her gaze.

She hurried over to Dumont. Frowning, he stepped to one side, letting her precede him into his office. When she was seated, he moved behind the massive desk, and for the first time she noticed the grim look around his mouth. He plucked up a long brown manila envelope from his blotter. "Miss Curtis, I presume you know what this is?"

Suddenly Kim had the inexplicable feeling that something heavy was about to land on her. "Clippings," she said, and heard the strain in her voice.

"Yes, Miss Curtis, clips. They're every reporter's most vital tool, next to his intelligence, that is."

Kim crossed her legs, then uncrossed them. The uneasy feeling wouldn't go away. "I'm afraid I don't know what . . ." Her voice faded. For a moment she'd had the distinct impression that he was looking at her legs.

But she must have imagined it. His face was withdrawn, completely impersonal. "Miss Curtis, yesterday you claimed to have given this paper its full quota of work. It appears you weren't being precisely truthful."

"I am always truthful, Mr. Dumont."

"But the fact remains that yesterday you did not fully perform your duties for this newspaper."

She felt her cheeks burning helplessly. "I have no idea what you're referring to, Mr. Dumont! Yesterday I was sent out on a story. I got it, and returned to the office and wrote it. The city editor, in fact, complimented me on it. It appeared on the front page. At which point did I fail to perform my duties to the paper?"

Dumont brandished the packet of clips. "In the course of writing about this put-upon family forced by society's indifference to live in a tent, did you at any time happen to check with the library?"

"The library? Well, no . . . it didn't seem necessary in this case."

"But a newspaper's library is a reporter's biggest tool, isn't that right? It's there so you can check the past histories of the people you're writing about. Agreed?"

A dim feeling of wariness was creeping over Kim. Could it be? Had Gus Filo possibly pulled a fast one on her?

"That's right, of course, but—"

"But you didn't bother to check out the Filos." Dumont's mouth tightened. He tossed the packet of clips across the desk. "Read them and weep, Miss Curtis. You'll find your Mr. Filo has played this game before. He's a skilled bunko artist, known to the police in Upper Washington and in the southern part of Texas. He's pitched his tent and made his crooked pitch, in both sections, and now he's moving in on the Northeast. He's done amazingly well—collected as much as two grand in one place—helped along, of course, by the gullible. And yesterday he met up with a gullible reporter. I regret to say a *Recorder* reporter."

Kim felt as if the world were tilting and she was about to slip off its edge. Why on earth had she failed to check the clips? She knew it was basic—how had it happened to slip her mind?

"I'm sorry, Mr. Dumont. I do check normally. I-I suppose when I saw that baby and those children it never occurred to me that a parent would deliberately expose children . . . *use* them. . . ." She steeled herself to meet his flat eyes. "It was stupid of me. Worse, it was unprofessional."

"Correct on both counts. A reporter shouldn't be capable of being hoodwinked. You'll remember I talked to you just the other day about looking at things coldly, realistically."

"I *do*—I usually do! But somehow on this story . . ."

He didn't seem to hear. His eyes had moved from her to some distant point on the wall. "I believe I made it plain that I expect quality work from quality people. Anyone who can't meet those standards I consider a drawback to this paper."

Kim could almost feel her face pale. "I don't believe I'm a drawback to the *Recorder*," she said in a choked voice. "And I'm sure the city editor doesn't, either. It isn't as if I've ever made this kind of mistake before."

He had turned away to fumble with a desk drawer. "Perhaps you were too occupied with other matters at a time when you could have been checking the clips."

"Other matters?" she said blankly.

He still didn't look at her. "Matters that had no business in an office."

As his meaning slowly sank in, fury made it impossible for Kim to do anything but clench the arms of her chair. When she was able to speak, her voice was tight with anger. "How ungentlemanly can you get, Mr. Dumont? And how unforgivably personal—and stiff—and . . . boorish! I feel sorry for this paper if it turns into a reflection of your personality. It will not only be deadly dull, but completely inhuman! And I feel even sorrier for the people working under you. I assure you, I won't be one of them! I don't have to take this kind of treatment!"

Jumping up, she moved blindly to the door. She couldn't believe this, couldn't believe any of it.

He was at her side before she could put her hand on the doorknob. "Now, look here." His hand came down, manacling her wrist.

She had to tilt her head back to see his face. "Mr. Dumont," she said, "I've accepted the blame. I did a sloppy job, and I'm sorry! But it wasn't because I was occupied with 'matters that had no business in an office,' as you put it. I had already handed in my story when my visitor arrived. I refuse to be scolded as if I were a schoolgirl, and I will *not* be told to punch a timeclock! Start asking your reporters to do that, and you'll have an empty city room! Furthermore, I've given hours of free time to this paper. I owe the Recorder absolutely nothing—and you less than that!"

"I didn't intend—"

"Your intentions don't interest me! And kindly let go of my wrist!"

He released her then, his face slightly flushed, but his body was still half blocking the path to the door. Even in the midst of her anger, Kim felt terribly aware of that body—aware, too, of a strange melting in her own body, a kind of helpless spasm somewhere in her, as if a part of her were saying All this talk has nothing to do with anything, as if a part of her didn't care in the least what this man said as long as he was close to her.

Her cheeks stung under the impact of her puzzling dual reaction. With a tremendous effort, she dove around Dumont, plunged through the doorway into the city room.

I will not cry, I will not shed one single tear, she told herself. And she didn't. She blinked back all the moisture. But she knew what she was going to have to do. And the thought of it broke her heart.

At a half-hour before deadline, she turned in her final story. Then very quietly she began to empty her desk.

After a while she was conscious of Wally standing behind her, screwing his eyes up as his cigar's grey plumage wreathed his face. "I get the feeling you're about to do something foolish," Wally growled. "I don't remember saying I was firing you."

Kim went on stuffing papers in her briefcase. "I'm firing myself, Wally."

"That's a kind of dumb thing to do. So you blew a story. Everybody does one time or another. What did Dumont say? I'm sure he didn't tell you to pack up. Matter of fact, he thinks you're pretty good."

"Don't con me, Wally. I've been conned quite enough this week."

"I don't con people. That piece you did Tuesday on the guy who grows mushrooms in his living room— Dumont told me he liked it."

"Good. I'm glad. At least I'll leave him with one happy memory."

Wally stood looking at her for a moment, then walked away, shaking his head.

And suddenly she felt herself weakening. She felt tempted to change her mind. Behind Wally's expressionless face and raspy voice, she knew he was really bothered at the thought of losing her.

And she would miss him, miss all of them. She loved this messy, noisy, busy newsroom where she'd gained a real knowledge of her craft. She loved Don, the beefy man at the copy desk who could recite Shakespeare in five languages. She loved the scrawny, smitten copy boy who often walked blocks out of his way to bring her Philadelphia sticky buns. She loved her battered desk and Ted, the shoeshine man, who showed her pictures of his pet parakeet.

But Jon Dumont had treated her unfairly and without respect, with an almost personal hostility. It would be pure masochism to stay here when she could get another job tomorrow—just walk across the street to the *Post*, or apply at the paper across the river in New Jersey. Or any paper anywhere in the country, for that matter.

Suddenly her hands were trembling. Out of the corner of her eye she saw Dumont enter the newsroom. He stopped, turned his head and glared fiercely in her direction. She pretended not to notice, but even now, as she was filled with bitterness for him, there was the familiar phenomenon going on: the same wild helpless hammering in her chest. He was the only man who had ever aroused such a feeling, and it was suffocating, completely overwhelming, a sensation she couldn't seem to shake.

Turning her back, she slammed her desk drawer shut and stared studiously at nothing.

When she looked up again, Dumont was gone. What had he been thinking, standing there staring at her?

Grimly she collected her morning's purchases—the cocktail outfit that would never see the penthouse suite of Walnut Towers—and stood watching the hands of the clock until it was seven o'clock.

Then without a backward look she hurried out of the newsroom. She wasn't going to say a single formal goodbye, because that would be her undoing.

"Mmm . . . looks like somebody's been buying goodies. I bet for the big shindig," Carol Prince said, when they met in the elevator. "Going to be lush, I hear—Le Petit Chef is doing the catering. Makes my mouth water to think of it."

Kim nodded and smiled her way down to the lobby, then waved goodbye at Carol and ran for a passing taxi. Huddled close to the window, she felt a sudden overwhelming weariness. A shock reaction, she knew. It didn't help to find herself staring down at somebody's forgotten newspaper, that morning's *Recorder*. Gus Filo's fraudulent, pitiful face stared up at her from the front page.

She had felt so happy writing that story, earning one of Wally's rare compliments. And then she had breezed out to the reception room to see Alan, and Alan had kissed her. Obviously Dumont had opened his office door and happened upon them.

Why should it have bothered him? Now that she had

time to think about it, his reaction seemed outlandish. Affairs were so much a part of the newspaper scene, even interoffice *amours*. There was always some torrid romance going on; nobody thought twice about it. In the newspaper business one's personal life was strictly personal. Nobody tried to make rules for anybody else.

And Dumont certainly wasn't a provincial, somebody moving in from a more uptight world. He hadn't come from, say, a banking firm, where everything was cut and dried, eternally marching to a predictable rhythm.

No, there must be another reason for his reaction, Kim told herself. Perhaps, since he claimed the *Recorder* was having money problems, he was looking for an excuse to start slicing the personnel. And the easiest, most logical place to start economizing would be with the youngest writers.

Her mind refused to go on with the thought. She was just too weary, and also too aware of the drama enacting itself in her imagination, a little play that could be titled *Portrait of Jon Dumont*.

Even now, as she gazed out at the buildings going by and caught the graceful clock tower of Independence Hall, all she really was seeing was Jon Dumont.

And she was still seeing him a few minutes later, as she mounted the stairs to her apartment, and as she tossed her packages to the sofa and as she moved into her kitchen. The same scenes kept unfolding: Dumont striding down a corridor, or turning to stare at her with his penetrating hazel eyes. Dumont in his rolled shirt sleeves, his hard tanned arms holding her gaze, making her pulse quicken. The man's image was swarming all over her and there didn't seem to be anything she could do about it. It was like being possessed, a kind of insanity. There was no sensible reason to be so absorbed with Jon Dumont, to have him constantly moving behind the scrim of her imagination.

Kim had never enjoyed drinking alone, but after she had had a hot shower, she poured a generous helping of Scotch from the bottle she kept handy because it had been Alan's favorite drink. It was fine, mellow Scotch, swift to act. A short while later she was stirring her dinner omelette with a little too much fervor and salting her vegetables with off-balance abandon.

Just as she was about to sit down and sober herself with dinner, the buzzer sounded. She answered it and looked through her peephole, expecting to see Megan in her orange jogging suit. But it was Jon Dumont.

Shock held her there, staring through the one-way viewer. Although she struggled to stir herself to action, all she could feel was an irresistible impulse to stay where she was, to keep on looking through the glass triangle, studying Dumont at her leisure. Unless she could thoroughly examine this tanned, rough-hewn face—a face just slightly off-balance, one eyebrow tilted higher than the other, a nose faintly hawkish—how would she ever determine what it was that so fascinated her?

So she stood taut, peering out, scarcely breathing, taking in the heavy eyebrows, the longish, mobile lips, the jutting chin. Was there something in this face that stirred her because it reminded her of her father, or some half-forgotten childhood friend?

She could discover nothing. Jon Dumont simply looked like Jon Dumont, someone she didn't really know and wanted terribly to touch. It was new to her, this need, this aching persistent wish to let her hands explore a man. She kept imagining her fingertips touching his crisp dark hair, sliding along the strong curve of his forearms, the broad terrain of his chest, the flat taut valley of his abdomen and then on to his long athlete's loins.

Her heart jumped willfully at the thought. Swinging her head away, she averted her eyes from the waiting face on the other side of the door.

Then the bell rang. She jumped and found herself furiously pressing her palms against the door, as if holding back a vanquishing horde.

Why had he come? Suppose she simply ignored him?

But he must hear the stereo, catch the odor of slightly burned toast. And all her lights were on. All right, it was obvious that she was at home, but that didn't mean she had to be at home for *him*. The man had insulted her, falsely accused her. *But if he went away now, she might never see him again.* The thought almost stopped her heart.

Tightening the sash of her robe and trying to marshal her quickening pulse, she opened the door.

He stood very still, looking down at her. Then his eyes swept past her, surveying the small room almost warily.

"The way you look"—Kim tried to make her voice sound bright—"makes me feel this crazy impulse to say, 'It's okay—the coast is clear.'"

His lips twitched, but his eyes stayed cool. "A man has to be cautious, stepping into enemy territory."

Feeling a need to break the connection with his eyes, Kim moved back from the door. "Enemy territory.

Yes, I guess it is." She was relieved to be recovering some shreds of poise. "However, I've been taught to be gracious under all circumstances, so if you don't mind competing with my dinner, come in."

"A lukewarm invitation, but still it's better than I have a right to expect." His grin startled her. His admission sounded utterly sincere, and it disarmed her.

Just inside the door he slipped out of his trenchcoat. Instead of handing it to her as Alan would have done, he carried it to the closet. As he hung it up, he looked unintimidating for a moment—a little tired and rather nice, Kim thought, realizing she had never before seen him out of the office. At the moment he could be any young husband returning home after a busy workday.

Husband? "May I offer you some coffee?" She gestured to the oval table in her combined living room-dining room.

"Coffee sounds great. It's working toward a winter night out there." He sat at the place she indicated. She saw his eyes taking in the floor-length Laura Ashley tablecloth, the pewter plates she had found in a Pine Street antique shop, the dried blue and gold flowers that echoed the design in the draperies.

"Miss Curtis—Kim—before I accept your hospitality, will you accept my apology for what I said today? I was unreasonable about your . . . visitor. I realize that now. And your error in the Filo story . . . it was one even a veteran could make. I overreacted to both situations for reasons that had nothing to do with you. You know, you kick the tire because the car doesn't work."

Kim looked at him, then glanced away quickly and reached for the coffeepot. "I suppose I should say thank you and pass it off, but I'm not going to. You owed me that apology." Her hand shook as she poured for him. Standing alongside him, she noticed the way his hair grew at the nape of his neck; it had a faint shimmering wave she hadn't noticed before.

At that precise moment he looked up at her. She knew he caught the intensity of her gaze. "Tough lady, aren't you?" he said. "Are you always like that?"

"Not always." Her voice had a drowned sound. Now his eyes were quite openly sweeping over her, touching her still-damp hair, the white expanse of her throat and chest revealed by the V of her robe, the swelling line of her thigh, sensuously outlined under the lustrous red velvet.

Something locked in her throat. She sank quickly in her seat, thankful that her half-eaten dinner gave her something to do. The omelette had turned cold and unappetizing, but toying with it gave her time to tamp down the incredible words that for one horrifying second had clamored to burst free. *Hold me, I'm dying for you to hold me!*

Swallowing a forkful of food, she then sipped her coffee. Finally she risked a glance at him. How serene and in control he looked. Never in this world would he be able to imagine the storm inside her, the persistent feeling of yearning.

"You see," she heard him say, "what I did was pass the buck to you. I had just finished the grim business of going over our financial report for the last quarter. Right after that I happened on a piece in *Editor and Publisher* about the number of newspapers falling by the wayside. Did you know it's an epidemic? I was in a foul mood and started out to the reception room to call

Cookie in for a memo—and you were there with . . ." He waved a hand back and forth, as if erasing the rest of the thought. "Anyway, my reaction was unreasonable, dumping on you for things that you had nothing to do with. You were a scapegoat, pure and simple. As soon as you left my office, I realized I'd been damned unfair." Abruptly he reached across the table and closed his large hand on hers. It was the lightest, most casual of gestures, a friend's reassurance. And it burned through her like high voltage, jolting her whole body.

Under his eyes there were little sprays of freckles he must have had since he was a boy.

"I'm sorry, Kim Curtis," he said in a low voice. "I hereby formally apologize. You're a hard worker, a terrific little girl reporter—"

"Uh-oh. Hold the stereotypes, Mr. Dumont." Kim raised a reminding finger.

He laughed. "Sorry—a terrific full-sized *woman* reporter." His hand dropped away from hers, and he continued. "Anyway, when I realized that you were emptying your desk—incidentally, Wally was quite worked up about it—I knew I had to talk to you privately. So I walked over here, my main purpose being to ask you to refill those desk drawers first thing tomorrow. In fact, I left the office so fast I didn't even get the two-star edition. Do you happen to have one around?"

It was so unexpected, and yet such a typical newsman's reaction—no matter what happened, he had to see the most recent edition of the paper—that Kim found herself laughing. "Help yourself." She waved at the coffee table.

"Will do . . . in a minute." He glanced at the window. "Say, what happened to all your blue flowerpots? They looked nice all lined up there."

"I moved them so the super could fix the window—" Kim broke off. "How did you know I had blue flowerpots? You've never been here before."

A dusky flush stained his cheeks. "Oh, I happened to look up at your window one day when I was walking by. . . . The sun was shining; you couldn't help noticing the line of blue pots."

"Oh." She stood up, needing to move away so she could think clearly. Something about what he was saying didn't make sense.

In the adjoining kitchenette she fumbled with a slab of cheese and said scratchily, "But . . . how did you know I lived here?"

They were only six feet or so away from each other and she saw the peculiar way he was looking at her, as if his eyes were trying to speak. Concentrating on the cheese, she heard the scrape of his chair.

Without knowing why, she found herself backing up, wedging herself defensively into a corner, the hard security of the wall somehow comforting. "Pears," she managed, "pears with some cheddar . . . ?"

But there was no way to divert him. He was directly in front of her now, not a hand's breadth between them. "I was thinking about you"—his voice was oddly hollow—"I was home one day. I looked you up in the phone book, then I walked over here. . . . In the vestibule it said you lived in 2A."

Even before his arms closed around her, his body had met her body, pinning her flat against the wall. With the impact, her bones seemed to shrivel, her muscles lose their ability to move. It was as if the touch of his body were dissolving all the complicated mechanisms that held her together.

"I'm the world's biggest liar." His voice was rough, husky, as he looked down at her. "I wasn't thinking about finances when I blasted you. I was thinking how much I resented anyone who had the right to touch you." His hands moved along her shoulders and down her arms to her waist. His body pressed harder against hers, his incendiary body that made her flesh flame in answer.

"*He* was doing what I wanted to do," he murmured, "what I've wanted to do since I first saw you."

His mouth closed on hers, seeming to almost absorb hers, and Kim stood for a moment in stiff disbelief, half expecting his low, mocking laugh to proclaim that once again she was allowing herself to be hoodwinked.

But the touch of his fingers on her throat was inexpressibly gentle, seductive as softly lapping water, and his mouth was gentle too, his tongue yearning delicately over the indentation of her upper lip like a butterfly courting a flower.

He gave a long sigh. Then abruptly the kiss deepened, and now she felt an urgency in him, felt the hard thrust of his lean body. A sudden weakness invaded her, as if her backbone were melting. She told herself it was all too much, too soon, but her mouth continued to hungrily drink in the sweetness of his kiss.

"You're lovely," he breathed. "Hair like early autumn leaves . . . I've been trying to find a name for the color of your hair."

She looked speechlessly up at him, dizzied, still disbelieving. His body had moved slightly away from hers, and she felt a terrible deprivation. She was startled at the feeling, at the rush of desire to reach out, pull him back, once again feel his iron hardness.

He was looking intently at her, and she had the feeling he had read the desire in her eyes, because all at once he was gazing past her, into the dim yellow-lit bedroom. "Shall we shift scenes?" His voice was light, and as he spoke he twirled a strand of her hair around his finger, as if playing with a toy.

The gesture and the tone of his voice seemed unsuitably casual, almost flippant. Kim felt herself stiffen. "You mean, shall we walk out of this dull movie and take in a ballgame instead?" Her voice was harsher than she meant it to be.

His hand fell from her hair. "You really think I meant it like that?"

She looked away, suddenly confused. "Well, quite a number of men do," she mumbled.

His face tightened. He grasped her arm almost painfully. "I'm not a number of men. Remember that."

She was silent, caught in the intensity of his gaze.

"I don't suppose you'll believe me when I tell you you've been working yourself into the corners of my mind," he murmured. "I had an idea that maybe the same process was going on in you."

Kim felt a rush of shame at her cynicism. "Well . . ."—she gave a faint laugh—"I'll admit one thing: I looked up *your* phone number too."

"You see?" His lips curved, showing his spectacular teeth. "We're more or less of a single mind. So what's there to prevent a delightful evening?" His hand fell from her arm and moved to the V of the velvet robe.

Parting its folds, his fingers lightly circled the outline of her naked breast, then slowly traced their way down to her knotted sash. "Suppose we just untie this, get you a little more comfortable. . . ."

"I'm quite comfortable the way I am, thank you." She aimed a level, icy look at him and stepped away, breathing heavily, as she tightened her sash.

"I don't get it." His eyebrows were furrowed. "I don't usually misread signals."

"Signals! I wasn't sending any signals!"

"No?" His eyes moved from her face to her breasts and then traveled insolently over the rest of her. "Every time you walk across that city room, you're signaling your sexual nature. A man would have to be blind not to see it."

"Some men see just what they want to see!" Kim strove to make her voice cool. But she knew her cheeks were flushed, and a charge of excitement was still going through her. "I don't know anything about you, except you sign my paycheck! I-I don't even know what your middle *initial* stands for!"

"I'll gladly divulge that information if it will alter the outcome of the evening."

The amusement quirking the corners of his mouth maddened her. "I'm really not interested—isn't that obvious?"

"You're not completely disinterested." Reaching out, he lightly touched her parted lips with a finger. "Not the way you kiss, lady."

Her heart leaped, but she kept her face expressionless. "I'll get your coat, Mr. Dumont."

She hurried to the closet, fumbled inside for his

trenchcoat, but as her fingers closed on it, she was conscious of a sudden pang. She had to force herself to turn and face him, hand him his coat.

He shrugged into it in silence and walked to the door. She couldn't believe he would leave without even a goodbye. She felt her mouth open to say something, anything, to hold him for a minute. . . .

Halfway over the threshold he turned. "I'll probably ring your doorbell again someday when I happen to be passing by. I don't give up easily; it's a family trait." His smile was brilliant, startling. He looked like someone who had just enjoyed a fabulous evening. "Will you save me some pears and cheddar for the next time around?"

Kim's eyes widened in astonishment. Save some pears and cheddar—he was deliberately reminding her of the moment when, helpless and boneless, she had wedged herself into a corner, knowing he was going to kiss her!

"Well, do I get a raincheck?" Jon Dumont said, the brilliant smile still firmly in place.

"You-you get a . . . a *maybe!*" Kim cried, and quickly shut the door.

It wasn't what she had meant to say at all. She stood with her back against the door, her hand covering swollen lips that still stung from the onslaught of his kisses.

Chapter Five

The next day Kim alternated between two moods. Part of the time she was in a dream, remembering that sudden kiss in the kitchen, and the rest of the time, as she tore out on assignments that took her from the art museum to the city morgue, she worked at shoring up her indignation against the man who had so blatantly tried to bed her.

Of course she realized persistence was an unavoidable part of the masculine psyche, but at least Dumont could have approached the matter a little more gradually! He had assumed that because he felt ferociously sexual, she must feel a matching fervor.

Well, didn't you? her ever-aware consciousness chided, and she struggled to deny the fact that her heart had almost stopped when his hand had lingered on her breast.

I'll probably ring your doorbell again. . . . The words filled her brain, wouldn't go away. Every time the door to his office opened, she found her gaze flying in that direction, disappointment washing over her as the person exiting turned out to be a boy carrying wire copy, or an editorial writer coming from a confab.

Besides, she reminded herself, he'd said probably. Which was a nice safe word that could also mean never. Of the two, never was undoubtedly more accurate; he'd never come again. He wasn't a man who enjoyed being brushed off, and she'd done it rather successfully, hadn't she?

As soon as the clock reached 7 P.M., she grabbed a cab home. On the corner of her block she ran into the little delicatessen called Pop's Gourmet. She bought an enormous wedge of cheddar cheese and a half-dozen pears. Not just for him, she told herself. Pears and cheddar were staples; everybody in the world liked them.

But she was conscious of a waiting feeling that kept her ears straining for the sound of the buzzer or the peal of the telephone.

The evening stretched out, long and silent. Gloom hung like a pall over her as she finally undressed and slid into bed. She wished she didn't have such an efficient memory. She kept seeing the bold adventuring look of his eyes, the moist curve of his lips.

The next day she decided she would never spend another evening mooning. It wasn't her kind of thing. It never paid to slip out of character, let someone yank you out of what you really were. She told herself not to think about him, and she would probably hear from him. This illogical thought annoyed her and she turned away from it. She didn't need him, didn't want him.

Once she saw him on the curb, outside the *Recorder*. He was hurrying into a taxi. The lines of his lean body—even the back of his heel, slipping out of its tasseled shoe—sent an insane thrill through her, and she rushed headlong down Broad Street, struggling to fill her mind with a jumble of other things.

Obviously he had forgotten all about her. He had struck out with her, and decided a followup wasn't worth the effort. It was very simple, she told herself.

And then, one busy day when Kim was sent from one complicated assignment to another, she met him again. She was in the elevator, heading home, feeling utterly drained and ready for a quick dinner and bed. Just before the doors closed, he got aboard. By chance no one else was sharing the elevator.

Scarcely looking at her he said in a low voice, "If I take you to dinner at La Panetière at eight tonight, would you serve me pears and cheddar for dessert? I'll come by for you."

She stared at him. She wanted to say something about last-minute dates not being exactly flattering, or something cool and bright about her crowded calendar, but her throat was bone dry.

"I . . . all right," she said.

The elevator doors slid open on the second floor and some clerks from Classified got aboard, and there was just the sound of their chatter and somebody's peculiar, trilling giggle. Not another word passed between them.

Outside the building Kim glanced over her shoulder, but he was nowhere in sight. Apparently he had stopped to talk to someone in the lobby. For a moment she felt dizzy, uncertain. Had she imagined it? Had he really said he was taking her to dinner?

He had said eight o'clock, so she couldn't have imagined it. She rarely waited that late for dinner, since very often she went without lunch. This had been one of those days. She had had only coffee and a doughnut since breakfast.

But it didn't matter now. Suddenly she wasn't in the least bit hungry. Excitement was crowding out every other feeling.

La Panetière. She smiled. She had no idea how Jon Dumont intended to comport himself tonight, but at least he had chosen to compliment her by selecting the best French restaurant in the city, one she could never afford on her own.

Ah, the tools of seduction, she thought wryly, but she couldn't help being pleased. She found herself humming as she took a refreshing shower.

But then, faced with the contents of her closet, she suddenly turned panicky, trying to decide how she should dress for an evening she found hard to believe was actually going to happen. When she found herself incapable of deciding between a perfectly lovely violet silk chemise-type dress and a perfectly lovely silver jumpsuit, she took a deep breath, shook her head hard and announced aloud, "I will not be a silly, clothes-bewitched idiot."

Deliberately she closed her eyes and reached in the closet, letting her fingers make their random choice, which turned out to be her simplest and favorite outfit, a two-piece, pale blue angora sweater and skirt that was serene and soft, and always made her feel happy.

Predictably, the moment she slipped into the dress, her nerves felt soothed.

Then the buzzer sounded, and her heart began to leap all over again. With her hand on the doorknob, she thought: What will it be like? Maybe this time it will be completely different—and wonderful. Or am I building him up, making him into something he could never be?

The thought left her feeling awkward and self-conscious. In fact, for the first half-hour over champagne at La Panetière, they were both rather clumsy, mumbling "Excuse me" too often and moving from feverish animation to sudden sinking silences, in the intervals stealing searching looks at one another. But as the superb meal progressed, the tension eased, and when they had left behind the dignity of the high-ceilinged restaurant and were strolling through a mauve evening in Independence Square, he caught her hand and for some reason they both laughed and then everything took on a glow as bright as that of the colonial lampposts.

They meandered in the direction of her apartment. When they got there they sat on the sofa and put their stockinged feet on the coffee table and drank three glasses of wine, talking comfortably about Philadelphia's architecture. Eventually Jon said she had some beautiful architecture of her own; certainly she must realize that she had absolutely amazing legs. Kim lightly said they did a good job of getting her across streets and up and down stairs, but she felt an enormous happiness warming her.

Taking his feet down from the table, Jon reached out and took her wine glass away, setting it carefully alongside his glass on the coffee table. He turned and took her gracefully in his arms. In one smooth natural movement she felt herself enfolded by him. In his arms she felt fully contained and sheltered and somehow valued.

Slowly he lowered his lips to hers and they kissed. Usually, when a man kissed her for a very long time she quickly grew restless and somewhat bored. But this man kissed as if he had an investment in the project. He kissed her thoroughly, lingeringly, untiringly and perfectly, and with many variations on the theme. When they finally paused for breath, and to smile hazily at each other, she saw the blue figures of the digital clock on the table and was amazed to find she had been in his arms for more than an hour. And although her mouth was bruised and swollen, she felt completely capable of devoting another hour to the same enterprise.

He refilled her wine glass. "Your mouth," he murmured, "looks bee-stung." With an appealingly swaggering look, he added, "And I'm the lucky bee." He reached for her again, but this time his lips adventured, moved from her mouth to tease the narrow lane behind her earlobe, and Kim shivered in sweet torment.

"I haven't lost my vast interest in seeing the rest of your *ménage*," he murmured, looking into the bedroom.

She flushed and pulled away from him. "I thought I'd made it plain that certain areas are off-limits."

"You're sure?" His eyes roved over her face.

"You want me to put up sawhorses?" Her voice was bantering, but she avoided his eyes. Never in her life had she been kissed the way this man kissed her. He turned her into one long swath of velvet.

"You said at dinner you had to leave early," she reminded him. "You said you had a terribly important appointment in the morning."

He whistled. "That's right. I almost forgot. Morgan's coming."

"Who's Morgan?"

"Whitey Morgan. Only the best sportswriter in the country. I'm trying to persuade him to come to work for us. But look . . ." He swept a hand across his forehead, pushing his hair back. Kim found her eyes lingering on its crisp texture. "This is no time to talk about Morgan or the office—not now. Come back here. We were progressing so nicely. Let's keep up the good work."

She laughed shakily, determined to hold her ground. "Aren't you assuming a little too much?"

"I hope not." He handed her her glass of wine. "Drink up. Wine has melted stern hearts down through the ages."

"Mine is guaranteed unmeltable." To prove her point, she took a generous swallow. As she set the glass back on the table, he swept his arms around her, and in a moment his lips were returning to their skillful business, his tongue tentatively tracing and retracing a path over her mouth, then gently moving against her tongue, making a slow, teasing, tormenting entry.

And for a moment she was powerless, her body full of a new, sweetly dangerous languor. His mouth had an intoxicating liquor of its own. Strange, she'd never before realized how lovely kissing could be.

"Come on, let's go see your bedroom," he whispered. "We could set the alarm for seven A.M."

She had to struggle to look indignant. "I thought

71

newspaper men tried to avoid being repetitive." She was surprised at how light her voice sounded, and how blurred she suddenly felt, as if she were inhabiting a dream.

"Not tempted even a little?" he said huskily, his hands moving seductively on her shoulders.

She felt her heart thudding. "Not at all," she lied. "Long ago I decided I don't want to be in the position of waking up some morning and thinking, Why on earth did I ever do *that?* I don't imagine you'd enjoy that feeling, either."

"I find it impossible to imagine any man thinking that after a night with you." His hands were gliding on her skin. "You remind me of some rather spectacular things, you know . . . the Venus in the Louvre . . . a white sailboat in San Francisco Bay . . . a Hawaiian flower dancing in the breeze. . . ."

Kim had the uneasy feeling she wasn't going to be able to forget what he was saying. Most male compliments seemed part of a game, trivial trinkets cleverly dispensed. But for some inexplicable reason the words coming from Jon Dumont seemed special, rare pieces of porcelain that could never be duplicated.

"Well, if I can't convince you that the next room would be a worthwhile enterprise"—his voice was low—"at least you could come closer, be a little friendlier."

Smiling, he tightened his hold on her, and with a sigh she capitulated, all at once aware that the accumulated weariness of a heavy workday and the combination of champagne and red wine—quite a lot of red wine—was beginning to take effect. The outlines of the furniture seemed a bit blurred, and after a while, as his lips roamed over her, she let her head fall back, finding a comfortable niche among the sofa pillows. Now her eyelids felt like stones and she wondered vaguely if she would ever be able to lift them again.

She woke to the poignant sound of foghorns on the Delaware and found herself staring puzzledly at her arm.

Her arm seemed to be clad in fuzzy beige wool. It didn't make sense—she never slept in her old beige wool cardigan sweater.

And then she was sitting bolt upright in the bed, staring with alarm at the grey light around her, and her heart was pounding crazily. What had happened? How had she gotten into her bed?

And more to the point, had anyone *else* gotten into it?

She couldn't remember. Her head was full of a faint painful drumming. Desperately she tried to sort through yesterday. Scenes flashed by like old movie stills: the busy workday, the rush of deadline, the skimpy lunch, then the bubbling predinner champagne . . . and how many glasses of red wine after?

Jon. Remembering, her hands went to her lips. They were like bruised fruit. A spasm of remembered joy touched her, then quickly faded as she remembered his whisper in her ear: "Let's go into the bedroom—we could set the alarm for seven."

She peered at her bedside clock, but it was too dark to make out the time. Swerving her head, she stared at the pillow beside hers. That faint indentation . . . had it been made by a head?

She couldn't remember. All she could recall were the

kisses, how they had blended into one long velvet joy, how languorous they had left her. Nothing happened, she thought, nothing *could* have. Then she thought with a fluttering heart: But if it *did*, if somehow something had happened what would he think of her? He'd think she was a pushover. He's got a reporter working for him who's a prize pushover. Four glasses of wine and she's yours, or anybody else's.

He wouldn't think that way, he wasn't that kind of man. . . . Really? You're quite sure about that? an inner voice asked. After all, what did she know about him?

She stared down at the beige cardigan. It was only partially buttoned. Under it her lacy slip dipped low, revealing the full curves of her breasts.

Hot-cheeked she moved her legs testingly, then yanked off the bedsheet. Her pantyhose and panties were gone!

Her hand clapped over her mouth. She stared around the room, finally spotted the silken lingerie neatly folded on a chair.

Her throat was dry as sand. Sliding out of the bed, she padded to the bathroom and flung open the door, then drew back with a gasp.

"Good morning," Jon said. He was fully dressed, rinsing the soap off her razor. He looked cheerful and bright-eyed, suspiciously so. "Hope you don't mind my using your equipment. Sleep well?"

"Yes." Kim avoided his eyes. "You?"

"Never better."

Her throat grew tighter. "I guess the wine got to me. I had a rough day yesterday." She tried not to let him see the question in her eyes.

74

"You dropped off like a rosy-faced infant after his first Christmas. Sorry about tucking you into such an unglamorous garb, but if you own any nightgowns, I couldn't find them."

"It doesn't matter!"

"It turned much colder. I tried my best to keep you warm."

She stared at him. "What does *that* mean?"

He looked closely at her. Then he laughed. "Nothing ominous. I got up near dawn and put the quilt over you."

"Oh. Oh, thanks." She watched him putting the razor back, his movements precise and careful. "Got up from *where?*" she said raspingly.

He was quiet for a long moment. Then he turned slowly and put his hands on her shoulders and held her gaze. "What you seem to be thinking . . . I don't operate that way," he said. "You may not know much about me, as you have pointed out, but you can count on this: I'd never want anything, take anything, presume—unless I was sure you wanted it too."

Her face caught fire. "I didn't think . . ."

He gave an odd smile. "Sure you did. You know why? Because you *do* want what I want."

"I really think you presume—"

He held up a hand. "*In vino veritas.* Last night, dear lady, you invited me to stay with you, in so many words. It was the ultimate temptation, believe me."

"I don't believe you! And if I did, it's horrible of you even to repeat it! You know I had too much wine! If you were any kind of person—" Her voice broke and she felt tears starting in her eyes.

He folded a towel neatly and hung it on the rack. "I

remained where I was, on your very comfortable sofa, Miss Curtis," he said gravely. "Need I offer any more reassurance?"

Then abruptly, magically, his expression changed; his smile grew warmer and more relaxed. "Kim, look . . ." Taking her arm, he led her to the window, and parted the cafe curtains. "The first frost came last night. See the silver tracery on the glass? Fairies' handwriting we called it when we were kids." She felt his shoulder companionably nudging hers, and everything smoothed out when he said, "Hey, if you hurry, I'll buy breakfast." ·

They gobbled croissants at a charming, almost deserted restaurant facing the Delaware River. In the early morning light the water looked grey and sullen and the last brittle leaves of autumn scudded past the windows, but she and Jon smiled as if the view offered tulips and sunshine. They drank too many cups of coffee, and Kim realized he too was trying to break through the misty feeling clinging to them.

"Look," he said, "there's no way I can duck out of work today, but how about you? You still look a little spaced-out. Think you can handle eight hours of jangling phones and deadlines?" Reaching over, he wiped at her buttery mouth with his napkin. "Or should we endow you with a devastating toothache so you can go home and crawl cosily into your bed?"

"I don't think I feel like bed at this moment."

His lips curved. "There we come to the parting of the ways. We could have twin toothaches in the same bed if

Whitey Morgan weren't due at my office at nine-fifteen."

"Do you really think you'll get him to come work for us?"

Jon shook his head. "It won't be easy to swing. People are inclined to think it's a comedown, going from New York to Philadelphia, although I can't see why. This city has everything New York has, only it's gentled, aged in the wood, more human . . . a more graceful pattern of life."

Kim nodded, chin in hand. She liked his talking to her in this way, and hadn't realized he possessed such sensitivity. "We need that kind of thinking in this city. I'm sure it's going to make the *Recorder* a better paper."

Frowning, he crumpled his napkin. "That's my aim, of course. But it was good to get away from business last evening. You made me feel free again. You made me forget the mess I've got on my hands, the advertising we lost this quarter. You made me feel the way I used to when I was on the magazine."

"You felt freer on the magazine than you do on your own paper?"

"Sure. On the magazine I could forget the job at the end of the day. Here, knowing the survival of the paper depends on my decisions . . . in a way, it makes me a prisoner. If there were no paper, believe me, I'd have worked a lot harder to persuade you to spend today with me. And hopefully tonight." His hand covered hers. "Don't pretend you wouldn't enjoy it. Some things you can't hide, things revealed by the luscious curve of your mouth."

She looked up at him, struggling to prepare a flippant answer, but as their eyes met she was caught. For a moment all of her seemed to live in his eyes; she saw herself there, very tiny and very still.

He's not going to rest until I give in, she thought. And I'm going to have a terrible time trying not to. I'm bedazzled, there's no evading it.

She lowered her eyelids. When she glanced up again, she was startled by his brooding expression.

"What's the matter?" Without thinking, she put her hand on his arm, surprised at how it hurt her to see him looking worried.

He gave a half-shrug. "Look, I want very much to be with you, but . . . I'm a firm believer in clarity. If we should become involved with each other, I wouldn't want either of us to feel bound. I'd want us to feel free to say how we felt about things. And if either should start losing interest . . ."

Kim felt a little stab of hurt. "Nothing could be more hypothetical than this particular discussion. I have no desire to be deeply involved. Didn't I make that plain?"

"Sometimes we can't decide these things—they evolve by themselves. I'm hoping to see a lot of you, so let's work out a little strategy beforehand."

"Strategy?"

"Right. You're a sensible, professional *woman* reporter—see, I got it right this time. I know I can count on you to keep in mind that any relationship we might have would have to be kept under wraps."

"If I had such a relationship—and the operative word is if"—Kim carefully set down her coffee cup—"I wouldn't exactly mail out announcements."

"You know what I mean. That office is the world's biggest goldfish bowl. You can imagine the gossip and cynicism if the staff got wind I was running around with you. I'd lose their respect, and so would you."

Kim lowered her eyes. The idea of secrecy irked her, even though she knew he was right, knew she would positively wither if the people in the office thought she was the publisher's pet—or playmate!

"We can hardly travel to the Gobi desert when and if we go out to dinner," she said dryly. "Someone's bound to see us at places like La Panetière, or even here."

He turned in his seat to study the other patrons in the restaurant. When he looked back at her, his eyes were relieved. "I know some out-of-the-way spots where we can dine in privacy."

Something about it made her cringe. His secret love, she thought. The woman he sees only when night falls. . . . You're being ridiculously sensitive, she told herself. Going to dinner with a man hardly makes you a backdoor wife. He's just behaving sensibly—he isn't the kind of man who would want his emotions on public display.

"I'd hate to think I was the cause of any trouble for you, Mr. Dumont." She gave a slightly off-key laugh.

He brought his face closer over the tiny table. "Come here, trouble." He closed the span between them with a light kiss.

Then he was looking at his watch. "Got to get moving. Got a newspaper to save from a lingering death."

"Jon! It can't be that bad!"

His eyes were grave. "It's bad all right. That's why

I'm not letting anything interfere with the job at hand."

Kim felt her face stiffening. "I wouldn't want to be thought of as interference. Perhaps we would do well to go back to the starting point, be publisher and reporter —and keep it that way." She found herself wishing the words weren't so hard to say.

"That's exactly what we'll be at the office, at least. I'll treat you like any other staffer. Our social times will be a thing apart. Agreed?"

She hesitated, vaguely aware that what he was proposing might not be so easy. But she was caught in his gaze, and it melted her. "I guess we can make a stab at it."

But as he moved to the cashier's desk and she stood waiting, gazing at the surly river, she felt an increasing sense of unease. Was it because a secret relationship seemed unnatural and lacking in substance? And suppose she fell in love with him, deeply and lastingly in love? The very nature of love made you want to shout it out. Love was meant to be a celebration, not a dark secret. Love should be the way her lips had been last night, full and open and rich.

But what right did she have to assume that what was happening between them would ever blossom into love? Yet, as she gazed at the man standing a few feet from her, as she caught the line of his cheek and traced the symmetry of his mouth, a part of her whispered warningly, *"For you it's the only love there'll be."*

She shivered, and told herself it was the too-early arrival of winter.

Chapter Six

"It's lovely, Cookie," Kim said, as the secretary displayed the slate blue cocktail dress she had bought on her lunch hour.

"It's the first really fancy thing I've had in years." Cookie smoothed the gown back in its nest of tissue paper. "All my money goes into getting my mortgage paid off. But I just had to have something special to wear tonight in honor of Mr. Dumont!"

"It'll be perfect with your hair." Then, noticing the circles under the older woman's eyes, Kim added in an offhand way, "How are you feeling these days?"

"Nothing wrong with me that a face lift wouldn't take care of." Cookie grinned, showing the space between her front teeth, and instantly she took on her startling hoydenish look.

"See you at the party." Kim gave a little wave. Hurrying past Jon's open door, she resisted the impulse to look in, reminding herself of their decision to remain aloof during their working day. The only trouble was, the few hours they had shared at dinner last night hadn't been enough. Her eyes still yearned for the sight of him, and she had the frightening feeling that that would never change; she would never tire of his face, his laugh or his touch.

The elevator was packed. Everyone was eager to get home and get dressed for the much-awaited party at Walnut Towers. The promise of liquid refreshment and convivial company—the latter meaning, to newspaper people, more newspaper people—was enough to guarantee the success of any party. Tonight's affair would be something to remember, Kim thought, as she hailed a taxi. While the main purpose was to honor the senior Dumont, it would also mark a triumph for Jon. He had somehow managed to convince Whitey Morgan to leave New York and write his well-known sports column, "Morgan Says," for the *Recorder*.

It was a giant catch, Jon had exuberantly explained last night while they ate dinner in a decidedly out-of-the-way Mexican restaurant. Ever since the rumor that Morgan wasn't happy in his New York setup, Jon told her, half a dozen top newspapers had been trying to snag him.

Talking about his conquest of Morgan, Jon's eyes had been brilliant, his whole manner contagiously happy, Kim remembered now, as the taxi sped her homeward. She had been caught up in his exuberance, and had agreed to have an after-dinner drink in his apartment.

"Lady, this is a bonanza—winning Morgan over and now getting you to come home with me!" he'd exclaimed.

"Don't assume a thing. One drink is precisely what I have in mind, Mr. Dumont."

His eyes had challenged hers but he had finally given in. "You drive a hard bargain, Miss Curtis."

She assumed that she had made her point, but minutes later, when he unlocked the door and she stepped into his sand-colored living room with its wide penthouse windows looking twenty-eight stories down, she immediately felt herself tensing. As he hung up their coats, she stared down at the fabulous view: Rittenhouse Square's treetops on one side and the Schuylkill River on the other. She couldn't seem to still the flutter in her chest. Why had she agreed to come? If he touched her, tried to interest her in what so obviously interested him . . .

There was a strange heated feeling in her body. It was unlike anything she had ever experienced. Maybe it wasn't Jon Dumont she had to worry about—maybe it was Kim Curtis.

But she found herself relaxing as he led her around, giving her what he called "the grand tour." There were a number of striking paintings in the living room. Pausing before each, he explained how and why he had acquired it. Then he talked about a number of books in his extensive library, and showed her the original Damon Runyon manuscript he had bought at auction and later enclosed in Plexiglas. And although there was a tension between them that ignited each time their fingers touched or their bodies brushed, Kim felt the evening lending a new dimension to their relationship. He was sharing intimate parts of himself with her, and the warmth of it was wonderful.

"Now I *do* know what your middle initial stands for," she said, holding his framed master's degree, awarded to Jonathan Stewart Dumont.

"Well, then, we've overcome the final barrier, haven't we?" Smiling, he took the leather frame out of her hands and put it back on the bookshelf. He put his arm around her waist and drew her to him.

His kiss was slow, gentle yet insistent, and although she stood stiffly in his arms at first, she soon felt herself softening, her lips growing moist, parting like the petals of a flower. His arms tightened—she felt their hard possessiveness—and as her breasts flattened against his chest and his body pressed harder into hers, a wave of overwhelming desire washed over her. His hands began to slide over her hips, urging her even closer, and all at once she heard a strange sound coming from somewhere in her, a broken, bereft sound that almost frightened her. *"No,"* she cried, and pushed feebly at his chest, but he didn't seem to hear. His mouth had captured hers again, and this time his lips were fiercer, covering and completely possessing hers. And then dimly she became aware that he was gliding, as if in a dance, and she knew she was moving with him.

She didn't know how they got there, but suddenly she was in his bedroom, lying on the enormous bed, atop a marvelously fluffy down coverlet. His face was over hers, his breath warm and moist on her cheek, its tempo quickened by desire. She felt his fingers moving at her throat, loosening the filmy material of her blouse. His kiss brushed her nipple to life. "You're not escaping tonight, love," he murmured. "I'm pulling up the drawbridge, locking all the gates."

She stared up at him, the words reverberating in her consciousness. Suddenly she had a wild vision of herself behind bars, imprisoned by her senses and by a man she barely knew. She felt her body stiffening. It couldn't happen, it was intolerable. She was Kim Curtis, fast-walking, fast-thinking, getting places under her own steam. She wasn't someone who was a victim of whims or illusions, someone who let her pounding pulse turn her entire life inside out.

"Jon." She pushed up on an unsteady elbow. "I think I'd rather not, if you don't mind."

"Oh, love, don't think"—he laughed and nuzzled his face against her throat—"just feel."

"No! I'll *always* think! I'm not a jellyfish, some spineless creature!" Her vehemence lent her strength. Bolting upright, she wrested herself from his hands, ignoring the fact that her flesh still quivered from its contact with him.

"I certainly couldn't confuse you with a jellyfish." Giving a short laugh, he pushed his tousled hair out of his eyes and fell back on the bed, staring up at the ceiling. "I had the idea we were embarked on a voyage together, that it was as enjoyable for you as it was for me."

"I'm not ready to sign up for the full cruise." Kim managed a smile she knew was crooked, but hoped would lighten the tension between them.

His eyes studied her for a long moment, their expression rueful and somber. Then, sighing, he slowly got up from the bed. "What we reject, we lose," he said. "But as I told you, I'll never seduce you unless you give me a definite go-ahead signal." He grinned suddenly, mischievously. "But I'm going to work like the devil to get that signal. You can bank on it. And now, let me fix you a nightcap, my reluctant Miss Curtis."

Partly relieved and partly saddened, she sat on the edge of the bed as he went to the kitchen. Listening to the clink of ice cubes falling into a glass, she buttoned up her blouse, remembering the moment when she had been on the verge of throwing away all caution. There had seemed such a rightness about having his hands on her body—an inexorable feeling, a joyful glow, like a million pinwheels spinning around inside her.

But to give herself up for one fiery hour? To lose her identity, float boneless and weightless for a little while . . . and wake in the morning to find she could never be herself again, never content or complete? To walk around like a zombie, wanting him, aching without him, unable to think or function until he was with her again?

Because now she knew that was precisely what would happen. If she gave in to her desire for Jon Dumont, it would be like giving in to an addiction. She would need him with her always. She would never feel free again.

I want him for always. She felt the weight of it lying on her shoulders. *Always* had another spelling, she realized: marriage. It was a word she had avoided in the past. Even during her brief engagement to Alan, she hadn't been eager to discuss wedding rings or furniture or anything smacking of commitment. Marriage had been something to think about at some later date—much, much later.

But sitting on the edge of Jon's bed, feeling the unappeased desire still raging in her body, Kim knew that with him she would want nothing less than complete commitment. She would have to have it, if she were to go on being Kim Curtis.

And wasn't it possible, she thought with a flare of hope, that he would want something lasting too? If they could manage a boss-employee relationship while they were in love, wouldn't that indicate they had a better-than-average chance to make a marriage work?

"Hey, miss. You awake back there?"

With a start, Kim was plunged from the vivid memories of the previous evening back to the present by her cab driver's scowling face. Looking out the window, she saw they had already pulled up at her front door.

"Don't mind me!" Laughing, she hopped out. "I'm going to a party tonight, and furthermore, I'm in love!"

It was wonderful to make the admission, even if the only person hearing it couldn't care less. "Crazy in love!" She laughed again, running up the stairs.

A half-hour later, trembling with excitement, she stepped back to survey her radiant image in the mimosa dress she had bought with this evening in mind. The face she saw in the mirror startled her. For once she didn't yearn to be any other woman anywhere else in the world.

Smilingly she previewed how it would be tonight in Jon's thirty-foot living room. She would sip her drink serenely, flash smiles at everyone and no one would ever guess that just the evening before she had been sprawled on the host's bed, with the host bending hungrily over her. "Yes, isn't it a stunning apartment," she would chatter. "Yes, the food's magnificent, but I'm glad there's a salad bar for my waistline's sake!" Perhaps at that point Jon's eyes would meet hers, and the tiniest smile would flash between them—nothing that anyone would notice, but she would know he was remembering. Last evening he had shown her the caterer's French menu and she had suggested that perhaps the cream sauces would seem threatening to people on a fitness binge. Why not offer a salad bar too? That way everyone could sin just a tiny bit and enjoy the evening more.

"You're right, beautiful and brainy and right," Jon had said, and promptly phoned the caterer's to make the menu change. It was just a little thing, but somehow it had warmed Kim, made her feel the party wasn't just Jon's, but theirs, a joint enterprise.

No one will ever guess we're more than employer-employee, she told herself now, and smiled as she swept a dab of violet shadow on her browbone. In a way the shield of secrecy made things even more exciting.

She remembered Jon calling her "love." Had it meant anything or had he used it casually, the way Londoners did? If he had said *"my* love," she realized, it would have been an entirely different matter. But still, it was nice, having his voice pronouncing love in her memory.

Happily grabbing up her purse and expecting nothing but pleasure from the party, she took off.

It was a thrill to see the look on Edward Dumont's wrinkled face. He was obviously overcome with delight at being honored, and excited to be back among the people he felt most comfortable with—the reporters, rewritemen and editors he had known most of his life. He and his frail-looking wife, Jon's mother, held court in the living room, and as each guest arrived, the senior Dumont's eyes grew livelier. "Remember the time old Jack Shaw was sent to photograph the queen of England and he called out, 'Hey, queenie, look over here'?" someone reminisced. "Remember how the queen looked in that picture? Utterly astounded!" Someone else recalled the time a prominent politician's son was kidnapped. Edward Dumont had come into the newsroom, rolled up his sleeves and tapped out an open letter, which was printed on the front page and addressed to the kidnapper. "It was the letter in the paper that got to me," the kidnapper admitted in a phone call to the parents, after he had returned the child to their doorstep.

Reminiscences, camaraderie, good food and watching how the people grew more comfortable with Jon—it all added up to a perfect evening, Kim thought. At one point Jon passed her and said out of lips that seemed scarcely to move, "Love that dress," and she felt a delighted flurry of excitement. Her happiness increased as Jon's mother settled beside her, talking warmly, and she saw Jon's eyes alight on the two of them.

Whitey Morgan arrived after everyone else, posing on the threshold as if expecting applause, and Kim felt a sudden uneasy premonition she couldn't explain. She watched Jon, beaming affably at the sports columnist.

"Ah—New York's loss is our gain!" Jon said, hurrying to include Whitey in the festivities.

Not that the man needed any announcement to draw attention to himself; his costume was obviously designed to take care of that. He was a tall fleshy man with the mane of wooly white hair that had given him his nickname. Matching all the rest of him to his hair, he wore white from head to foot. Even his watchband was white. In a crowd of people dressed in autumn colors he certainly stood out, Kim thought, and her lips flickered wryly as she remembered that Jon had said, "I'm going to keep this fellow supplied with the best bourbon and fan his ego on the hour. He's got an enormous following. He could mean a lot to this paper."

Jon was certainly right about the ego, she thought, noticing how Whitey acted as Jon led him around the room, introducing him to the staff. It was like a presentation of a royal visitor, and Whitey grandly played up to the role, granting a brief handshake here, a smile there, sprinkling a few condescending words between gulps from his highball glass.

She found herself tensing as, inevitably, it came her turn, and she had to struggle to form a welcoming smile. Apparently, she was successful because Whitey picked up on her smile right away. His small pale eyes—were they trying to be white too? Kim wondered sardonically—flicked over her then seemed to settle permanently on her breasts. After a few minutes under this ardent surveillance, Kim hurried to the powder room to check if a vital seam had split or some other disaster had exposed more of her than was legal.

But no, her neckline was the same as it had always been, revealing just a faint hint of cleavage, nothing that would call for special attention.

Obviously, though, it called to Whitey Morgan. As she made her way to the long glittering buffet table with its circle of yellow chrysanthemums, she was aware that the columnist was following her. Pretending not to notice, she paused to study the contents of a silver casserole dish. Whitey paused too, his broad body nudging hers, although there was no reason to nudge. Nobody was crowding him.

Giving the man a wide berth, Kim moved to the other side of the table and meticulously transferred some smoked salmon onto her plate.

"Don't tell me *you're* on a diet." Whitey came right after her, his eyes still involved with her chest. "I can't figure it, all you gorgeous tidbits going on diets. Don't you know a man likes a full-fleshed female to hold in his hands?"

Kim lowered her eyes to hide her revulsion. "This salmon is delicious, Mr. Morgan. By the way, that's our city editor over there at the salad bar, Wally Forbes. I'm sure you'll want to talk to him."

"Why?" The sports columnist piled salmon on top of the mounds of roast beef on his plate. "City editors don't mean a thing to me. My stuff doesn't get edited. That's one of the rules I work under. Every page I turn in stays virgin." He leered over his dish at her. "And while we're on the subject, I hope you're not."

Kim looked disbelievingly at him.

"Well, what's the story?" He grinned wetly. "Are you or aren't you?"

"Aren't I *what?*" she shot back coldly.

"Virginal, of course. I hope not. I always hate any delay in reaching the goalpost."

Kim met the pale eyes deliberately and let her gaze move coldly over the man's fleshy face and body. "You're really quite revolting, Mr. Morgan," she said quietly. "And also very foolish."

She saw the livid anger flash in Whitey's eyes, but she didn't care. Her stomach felt knotted. What an appalling man—head over heels in love with himself.

Walking in a wide circle around him, she carried her plate to a chair near a window. She was thankful she would have little on-the-job contact with Whitey Morgan. His desk would be in Sports. Or maybe, since he was so important, he would write his column at home and phone it in.

She sat looking around Jon's living room. She loved it. Although it was modern and she preferred traditional, it somehow managed to be warm and comfortable. Maybe it was the wide wall of books, or the display of Jon's college athletic trophies or the table unashamedly devoted to family photos—his parents, his older brother who lived on the West Coast, his brother's four little boys.

Jon had pointed out the photos last night. "I'm crazy about those kids." He smiled at his nephews in their matching T-shirts. "Hope to see them soon. I'm due in Frisco for the publishers' convention. Say, are you any good at picking out presents for kids ranging from four to twelve years? I can't seem to find the time."

Kim had felt her cheeks warming. Shopping for the boss . . . she knew she should rebel against this stereotyped role, but this was different. This was Jon. This was personal. He was letting her into a private part of his life.

"I'm going shopping Tuesday," she said. "Suppose I bring some things in and you can look them over?"

Jon held up a hand. "Not to the office. Remember, we barely know each other."

"I forgot," Kim confessed smilingly. She had turned

back to look at the photos again, finding a dim reflection of Jon in the faces of his nephews.

Now, gazing covertly at him from across the crowded room and trying at the same time to give the impression that she was studying the Manet-type painting to the left of his shoulder, she saw that he and Whitey Morgan were in a huddle, talking intensely about something. How wonderful Jon looked in black tie. So clean and strong and alive, his hair so crisp and full. Her fingers could precisely remember the feel of it.

"Hi. That color's great on you." Carol Prince sank down onto the beige suede chair alongside Kim's. Carol's perennial turban had gone formal. It was gold lurex to match her jump suit. "Great-looking guy, isn't he?"

Kim wondered briefly if Carol had read anything in her face. "You mean the boss?" she said lightly. "I guess that's a fair description."

"Oh, come on, you can be more enthusiastic than that. If I were your age—"

"Talking about men"—Kim quickly rearranged the discussion—"what do you think of our new sports columnist?"

Carol twisted her mouth expressively.

And then the waiters brought in champagne and Jon toasted his father, telling everyone how Edward Dumont had taken over the reins of the *Recorder* from *his* father. "So now we are into our third generation as a family-operated paper, and that's something of a miracle in today's conglomerate world. To honor our former publisher and to send him merrily on his well-deserved retirement trip . . ."

Everyone oohed and aahed as Jon presented his

father with a clock-calendar-radio fashioned out of a gleaming silver replica of the *Recorder* building.

After that Al Sherman, the *Recorder*'s cartoonist, came forward to present the gift Kim knew the elder Dumont would prize most—an almost life-sized sketch of the publisher astride the world, his luggage autographed by all of the *Recorder*'s employees.

It was a warm, fitting end to the evening. "Great party, Mr. Dumont," people were murmuring, as Kim joined the line of departing guests. "Yes, it was just lovely, Mr. Dumont," she echoed when she reached Jon's side, and for a swift moment she risked meeting his eyes, expecting the usual barely discernible flare of warmth.

But his eyes stayed strangely and disturbingly flat. As she moved away, Kim found herself looking perplexedly back at him.

What on earth was the matter? He had looked at her as if she were someone he didn't want to know.

Had she imagined a tinge of antagonism in his expression?

From somewhere someone called her name and turning to give an automatic smile and wave, Kim let the chattering, laughing crowd sweep her to the elevator and through the lobby. Outside, wrapping her velvet coat closer, she paused to frown up at the amber penthouse windows.

Perhaps that cool look had been deliberate. Perhaps Jon had been afraid even a faintly friendly expression would give away his true feelings.

She felt herself flushing. Lovely things could be so easily spoiled and made to seem unlike the way they really were. What she felt for Jon was so beautiful.

Suddenly it seemed imperative that nothing should ever happen to change that feeling.

Oh, she was being ridiculous! Certainly he would phone, explain everything. He would be eager to go over the events of the evening, an evening she was sure had made him many new friends among the staff.

At her apartment she undressed and got into bed, waiting eagerly, trying to read. She waited till well past 2 A.M. but the phone never rang.

Chapter Seven

The next morning she was reaching for her showercap when she heard the sound she had been waiting for, the phone's shrill summons. Snatching up a towel, she raced to answer it, then sagged as Carol Prince's voice crackled in her ear.

"Kim—you hear the news?" Carol said ominously. "You know that gorgeous party the boss man gave us? Well, it turns out he was just softening us up for the kill."

"The kill?"

"Bailey phoned me. It's murder over at the office. Our last night's host just fired two reporters— Thurmond and Halsey."

"Is this a joke?"

"Not to Thurmond and Halsey."

"But Hal Thurmond! He's been on the paper at least ten years!"

"Well, he's out in the cold as of this morning. Of course I know he's half-sloshed most of the time, but he's got plenty of company in that newsroom. I have no idea why Halsey got nicked, do you?"

"Not the slightest."

"One thing I do know, the old man never did things this way," Carol said. "He always gave people fair warning. Can you imagine bouncing two at a time! Pretty dirty pool after all that talk last night about working together for the dear old family business. And another thing, nobody's ecstatic about this slug, Whitey Morgan. He's already demanding more special privileges than Russia gives the KGB!"

"Morgan's a big name, Carol." Kim heard the unconvincing sound of her voice. "He'll help the paper."

"Since when does the *Recorder* need help? It's making carloads. You saw the swank layout in Dumont's apartment; one of those suede chairs would buy me dinners for a year!"

Kim was tempted to point out that Jon had long ago earned his high style of living and that it had nothing to do with the paper's current financial condition. She censored herself just in time. Such an ardent defense would be far too revealing. Carol would immediately guess she had more than a casual link with the boss. Anyway, she had no right to discuss Jon's business with anyone.

Hanging up, she stood shivering in her bath towel. Two firings in one day. Now the whole office would be tense and more distrustful than ever.

How could he have done it, let people go without even a warning? He couldn't possibly be that callous. Certainly he must know that Thurmond had a family. And as for Halsey, he apparently had some kind of health problem. You didn't fire a man just for being sick.

If Jon had felt the firings were necessary, why hadn't he diplomatically spaced them out? How ironic that he would do something like this after giving his party! She had been so thrilled to see people warming to him, getting to see how wonderful he was.

Maybe he wasn't, though. She considered herself a good judge of character, but of course she had made a few mistakes with men—what woman hadn't? Alan, for instance. She'd certainly overrated Alan's character.

The buzzer startled her, and she pressed the door button without thinking. Peering into the viewer, she suddenly felt all the lights in the world blaze on again. Her hands flew eagerly to the lock—

Then halted, as she became aware of her skimpy bath towel sarong. Tearing into the bedroom, she whisked out the delft blue robe her father had sent from London. "Someone copied the color of your eyes," he had written.

For a flickering moment, unexpectedly, a picture flashed: the two men together, her father and Jon. They would instantly like each other, she was sure of it.

Or would they? She bit her lip, remembering the firings and reminding herself that the most charming people could carry callousness inside them, disguised by delectable smiles.

But the needling doubts fell away as she threw the

door wide and saw Jon's face. "Hi," she said breath-lessly.

He walked past her into the foyer, and she called gaily to his back, "What are *you* doing here? I heard you were at the office this morning."

"Yes, I guess you've heard. What are they calling it—Bloody Saturday?" He turned to look at her. Something in his expression made her smile thin, flicker uncertainly.

"Well, firings always make people buzz." She stared at him, wondering why he looked so distant.

He gave a shrug. "Nothing that has to concern you."

It was as if he had thrown up a barrier, topped it with a neon-lighted No Trespassing sign. "Well, I do work there," she said, trying to tamp down the hurt.

"As a reporter. Not an executive."

For a moment she thought he was making a joke, but as she saw the grim line of his mouth, she felt her hurt growing, making her want to lash out at him. "I certainly don't intend to interfere with your decisions," she said tightly. "I just can't help wondering how anybody could do that, fire two longstanding employees at the drop of a hat."

"They both deserved firing long ago, but I don't intend to discuss that."

"Your father never fired anyone!" The anger in her was steamrolling now; she couldn't hold it back. "He *always* gave people a second chance!"

"Look, do we have to go into all this?"

"*Yes!*" She knew she was overreacting, but she couldn't help herself. His manner was so unbelievably cold. "How can you march around acting normal after

99

firing men who worked for your father for so many years?"

His jaw tightened. Swinging away from her, he dug his hands deep in his pockets. "That's just the point. My father should have fired them long ago. Thurmond pretended to cover stories and never went near the scene; he used to sit in a bar and phone around for the facts. The whole staff was constantly covering up for that man. My father wasn't any smarter. He thought he was being kind, but actually he didn't have the gumption to let Thurmond go. Some shock treatment might have made the man wise up and fly right."

"What about Halsey? Did you fire him because he's chronically ill?"

He folded his arms across his chest and stared down at her. "Hold it—do you think I *enjoyed* this morning? Do you seriously think I wanted to let those men go?"

"Well, if you were so . . . so uncaring that you didn't even bother to give them a warning . . ."

"They've been warned many times before. I've seen their personnel files. My father knew that Halsey's 'sickness' always led him to the racetrack instead of a doctor's office." He shook his head almost wearily. "Which would you rather see—these two fired or four hundred and thirty people standing on line for unemployment compensation? Not to mention a city stripped of its best paper?"

"Well, of course I don't—"

"Look, I appreciate your feelings for your coworkers. I'm not exactly thrilled to be playing Scrooge. But I'm determined this paper will survive. The *Recorder* won't fall into the clutches of some damned conglomerate. If people can't do their work, they'll have to go.

We can no longer afford Dad's paternalistic view. If it's a matter of survival, I'll fire anyone. That's my final word."

"A matter of survival? Jon, I just didn't realize . . ." Kim spread her hands helplessly. "See, the people in the newsroom . . . I just care so much about them."

"Don't you think I care?"

She felt herself wavering under his steady look. "I'm sorry, Jon. I didn't mean to jump all over you. Here, let me take your coat."

But as he shrugged out of it, he pointedly refused her assistance. "Why did you do that last night, pull that haughty stuff, antagonizing Whitey Morgan?"

"*I* antagonized *him?*"

"You sure did. He said to me, and I quote, 'How come you have a nasty witch like Curtis working for you—somebody like that going out to deal with the public'?"

Kim's face burned. "You don't understand—"

"I told you it was important to keep this guy happy. All right, so he's a prima donna, but you didn't have to stick your fist in his ego."

"Didn't I?" Kim gave a jagged laugh. "The man was revolting and I told him so! What did you want me to do—climb up on his lap and pet him?"

"No, just use common sense, realize we need him a lot more than he needs us. Our readers' survey shows sports fans are as crazy about his stuff as they are about Philadelphia pretzels. We want this fellow happy there!"

"Well, don't count on me to pitch in for the noble cause! He made a play for me, a darn crude one. He didn't even pretend to dress it up!"

"You expect me to blame a man for that? I'm sure it's a common occurrence."

"But it's rarely done in such a blatant way, and I told him so. If you'd been there, I would have expected *you* to tell him!"

His lips curved oddly. "Would you? You mean you expect a publisher to go around defending his reporters against possible seduction?"

"Yes! If *you're* the publisher and *I'm* the reporter!" She heard her own words and bit her lip. "I mean . . ."

"You're doing precisely what I thought you were mature enough to avoid. You're injecting personal feelings into a business situation."

"Is it a business situation when an absolutely crawly character makes a play for a woman you supposedly value—at least to some degree?"

He looked sternly at her. "Let's stick to the subject: Whitey Morgan. Couldn't you have let him down lightly, controlled your feelings?"

"What amazes me is how well you control yours! Or maybe it doesn't take much effort. Maybe yours aren't that intense!" Suddenly the sight of his stranger's face was too much to bear, and a ragged, involuntary sound came out of her. Ashamed of it, she whirled away from him, not thinking of where she was headed, just needing to escape.

Lunging across the floor, she felt her bare foot slide—the prized patch of oriental rug was shooting out from under her. Her legs splayed in different directions, and the vase of flowers on the desk tilted along the wall.

She landed on her back with a loud thump, wincing at the impact. *"Oooh!"* Half crying, she reached down to tug at the flaring panels of her robe, which had parted to reveal her thighs, glistening whitely in the light from the windows.

"Are you all right?" She heard his quick step. Instantly he was kneeling beside her, his large capable hands slipping under her arms as he held her to him, his eyes worriedly scanning her face.

"I'm okay," she murmured. Then, as her fingers touched his face, she whispered, "Don't do that again."

"Don't do what?"

"Don't go away from me." The words were torn from deep inside her, from wherever her soul was.

And then he was bending closer, bending far over her to kiss her thigh, and the kiss turned into a torrent of kisses that made her gasp and clutch at him, her entire body softening. His mouth winged kisses all the way down to her toes and up again, kisses that made tiny flames leap along the length of her, and, as his mouth nuzzled the flesh of her shoulder, she sighed and murmured his name. She felt him slipping her robe from her shoulders, felt his face sinking against her breasts, and the longing in her flamed unbearably. His tongue circled the whorl of flesh around her nipple, and the flower petal softness tightened and peaked. She felt the hard edge of his teeth scrape her skin, but it wasn't painful—there was a strange beauty in it—and it seemed to typify his roughness and her fragility. "Kim," he said in a low urgent voice like a plea, and suddenly she felt herself locking her arms tightly around him. For a moment, clinging to each other, they swayed and stared into each other's eyes, and it seemed unthinkable, unendurable to ever let go.

"I'm going to put an end to your rebellion, my fiery

little antagonist!" His breath was hot in her ear as he swung her up into his arms and started for the bedroom. "I've got just the formula to keep you nice and amenable, at least for a little while."

Kim opened her eyes and looked up at him. Her breath was coming in struggling gasps; the emotion she felt was so intense that there were tears on her cheeks, but his words made everything come to a standstill.

"Nice and amenable?" she choked out. "Like the animals in the zoo? You'll throw me a tidbit and make me forget everything I am? My whole nature?"

He grinned. "Something like that. We're man and woman. That's all that counts at the moment."

"Wrong! I'm a person first, Jon! Let me down. I'm not changing my feelings about anything just because you've kissed me. Your kisses aren't that earthshaking!"

She was sorry the minute the words were out. She saw the stab of hurt in his eyes, and wanted to cry out *No, I didn't mean that. I'd rather be kissed by you than breathe!*

But no, if she gave in now, she would be giving in utterly, surrendering far more than her body. How could she give up her very selfhood for something with as little substance as the fluff on a dandelion?

If only he would tell her that his involvement went above and beyond this tiny tick of time!

"Well"—she heard the grating sound of his voice—"that little remark makes things pretty conclusive, doesn't it?"

Staring into his face she saw anger where hunger had burned, hunger that just a moment ago had roused in her not only an answering emotion but also a flicker of pride that she could elicit this storm of yearning in such a man.

"Jon, I . . ." She heard the frail quality of her voice and felt her fingers moving tentatively at his lapel.

But he seemed unaware. Abruptly she felt herself being lowered heavily, unceremoniously, as if she were a burdensome weight. "Is this some weird specialty of yours?" he bit off. "Saying one thing with your body and something completely different with your words? Do you deliberately set out to be difficult? Do you enjoy letting a man down?"

"You're calling *me* difficult?" She was conscious of the bereft feeling of her body now that his arms were gone. "That's really unbelievable after the way *you've* been acting!" Thwarted longing churned in her, mingled with anger. "If you don't mind, I'd like you to go now! I'm sure you have a lot of 'executive' matters waiting for your special attention!"

"That's true." His eyes were cold as stone. "And I look forward to handling them without benefit of gratuitous advice, Miss Curtis, much as you delight in giving it."

Sweeping up his coat, he strode to the door, opened it and was gone.

A week went by. The sun went down, the clouds came out and Kim's smiles were just polite, muscle-stretching grimaces.

Finally, the phone call came that made her sing, rush to the refrigerator and gobble nearly everything in sight, water her dying fern and really smile at herself and at everything in the universe.

The voice on the phone had said simply, "I'm sorry

about the other day, Kim. May I come collect you very early on Sunday and spirit you away?"

"Yes," she said breathlessly.

"It'll be cold," he said. "Dress warmly."

And now Sunday was here, and she was with him again, thinking that she felt happy, but wary. She was walking tiptoe on the edge of joy, fearful every minute that it would fly away again.

Jon had arrived in a shiny red compact, rented, he said, because he never used the business limo for pleasure. In fact, he preferred walking over riding any day. But now they were going far afield.

Far afield turned out to be New Jersey's deserted, chilly, lovely Cape May. His family's beach cottage was there, a comfortable old place with seashells on the window ledges, fishnets over the mantel and a fireplace that wouldn't draw. "Nobody's used it for a few years," Jon said. "We'll have to snuggle to keep warm. There's a snuggling blanket in the windowseat, if memory serves."

Crossing the room to take out the moth-eaten blanket, Kim found herself wondering about the snuggling. Did he have memories of long-legged bikini-clad girls wrapped in this blanket? She thought of the model he had gone skiing with, and wondered once again if the lady had endowed him with the tiny V-shaped scar on his forehead, a lifetime souvenir. Did he think of her when he shaved in the morning?

The thought annoyed her—it wasn't her style to worry about a man's former girlfriends! It was not only pointless, but demeaning. Did love change a person so drastically?

I won't let it, she told herself fiercely. I want to love Jon Dumont but I want independence too. I want mutual respect and equality in our relationship.

And, as the day slowly, miraculously, turned itself into something close to perfection, she began to believe that such a relationship might be possible.

She didn't know exactly what alchemy took place. Perhaps the sun's unexpected emergence through the thick clouds had something to do with it, but all at once both she and Jon seemed to shed their doubts and tensions. As they walked along the hard-packed sand and gazed admiringly at the resort's famous ginger-bread houses, as they stood in the midst of a hundred seagulls and wondered if the birds consciously missed the tourists' popcorn, as Kim's face turned a dusky pink from windburn, and as they stood on the rim of the frigid, lace-edged ocean and tried to picture what lay at the far-flung opposite shore, they became gloriously comfortable with each other, playfully tossing out thoughts and fantasies as they might toss pebbles in the water.

In the midst of all the lightness, Kim looked up into Jon's eyes and cried impulsively, "Don't you see? You hurt me when you didn't mind! You actually hurt me!"

"Didn't mind what?"

"*Whitey*—the way he talked to me."

"Who said I didn't mind?" He pulled her closer. "If I'd been there when he said it, he would have been *Bloody* Morgan. But where would that have gotten us, besides satisfying your natural feminine desire for my protection?"

Kim was smitten with a startling shyness. "Nowhere,

I guess. Don't tell me I'm basically just a foolish female."

"Not foolish—natural. The truth is, I'm flattered that I bring out the intensely feminine in you. But I also understand that I can't walk around that office charging into every man who makes a play for you."

"I know. I know here, anyway." She tapped her forehead.

"That's a beautiful cranium, and I hope to get to know some of the interesting thoughts flying around in it." He sighed. "However, I can't help wishing you worked across the street."

She glanced quickly at him. "Don't even think it! Don't you realize I'm very loyal to the *Recorder*?"

"But you have to admit if you worked for the *Post*, things would be a lot easier."

She stiffened slightly. "Easier for *you,* you mean. I hate the *Post*!"

"Okay, remind me not to fire you."

He was joking, of course, but she couldn't resist the temptation to mention something that had been worming around in her thoughts.

"Jon . . . in the future . . . why not let Wally do the firing? I mean, the city editor usually does, and it would be so much easier for you. It wouldn't make you look like . . . like everybody's enemy."

"No." His lips tightened stubbornly. "I'll handle my own dirty work. Fortunately, though, I don't see the need of more dismissals . . . at least not at the moment." He gazed soberly down at her. "Hey, this is our time, yours and mine. Do we have to talk about the office? I can think of at least a million more important matters to discuss—like exactly what shade of blue *are* your eyes? You realize I'm not really sure?" He spun her around so the full light of the sun touched her face. "Ah, yes, a very unique shade. Some violet in the blue, and grey . . . and tiny glints of gold. What fascinating eyes you have, love."

Love. The casual word again, but it had the softest, most cherishing sound. Someday would he go a step further, call her "my love," really claim her? And now his lips were gently finding hers, and after the kiss he said gravely, "Look, let's keep out everything extraneous today, just wall it off. Let's have this time to let things flower. I don't mean just the sex part. I realize I've rushed you before you were ready. And besides, I'm beginning to see there are many other sides of you that I'd like to know, if you're willing to let me try. . . ."

His sincerity was stamped on his face, and the sight made Kim's heart leap. Was there a suggestion of a promise in his words? "I'm willing," she said softly.

Huddling against the rising wind, they walked to the Victorian hotel that served homemade barley soup and fat wedges of just-baked bread and the sweetest boiled lobster in the world. After dinner they wandered around the lobby, looking at old sepia photos of bewhiskered, early Cape May citizens and plump bathing beauties in long john bathing suits, and they puzzled over intricate bottled ships. Their smiles kept converging, as Kim thought, It's going to be all right, it's going to be better than all right. Why was I doubting it?

Jon deposited her at her apartment shortly before

midnight. A half-hour later the All Nite Flower Boy's distinctive heart-emblazoned truck arrived, and the deliveryman left Kim three dozen blushing pink roses. "Today was a time apart," Jon had written above his black, square initials.

Calling herself a sentimental idiot, but smiling just the same, Kim tucked the card under her pillow.

Chapter Eight

Kim juggled her armload of boxes and relievedly said goodbye to the toy department of Copley's Department Store. She had spent the morning looking for suitable gifts for Jon's West Coast nephews. The experience made her wonder how mothers managed to survive shopping for four boys whose interests ranged from dump trucks to Vatican City stamps.

But despite her aching arches and overburdened arms, she wasn't complaining. Her world had taken on a glow and glitter; she found herself smiling foolishly whenever her thoughts drifted back to Jon. He had been so sweet, so attentive last evening. In fact, ever since their Cape May Sunday there was a new, deeper shading to their relationship. He listened more closely to what she said, seemed to want not only to look at her hair and smile and legs, all of which he frequently complimented, but at her *feelings* about things.

Would he suggest going to Cape May again soon? The thought made her breath quicken. She would cook a dish she had just learned to make, chicken in white wine with olives and almonds. They would get out the snuggling blanket and be very close, and if he should ask her to be even closer . . .

How on earth would she manage to go on resisting? If his fingers simply grazed her skin, her entire body responded; she could actually see her skin take on a rosy flush.

Last night when that had happened, he had promptly moved away from her, trying to hold onto his promise, letting her know he was waiting for a sign from her.

And now, glancing down at her packages, Kim remembered that he would be gone this Sunday. He would be three thousand miles away. After addressing the publishers' convention, he would visit his brother's family in Napa Valley. Five whole days—how could she manage to get through them?

Of course you'll manage, she told herself stringently, thinking how crazy it was that just a short while ago Jon Dumont hadn't meant anything to her; he was simply "the boss's son." How could one person change her world so much?

She was at the store's revolving doors when, out of the corner of her eye, she saw the tweed cap.

It was made for Jon, she realized that immediately. He had the perfect face for a cap. And combined with his herringbone blazer . . . one night she'd peeked into his armoire and particularly admired that imported blazer. And now that it was almost his birthday.

He'd be amazed that she knew his birthday! She had been looking up clippings in the library when, on impulse, she had checked to see what was filed under *Dumont, Jon*.

There had been exactly three clippings: one announcing his graduation *summa cum laude* from Princeton, another telling of his appointment to the staff of *Today* magazine and a final piece dealing with his succession as publisher of the *Recorder*. A brief biographical note revealed that he would be thirty-five tomorrow.

It had seemed very important, knowing the day he was born. She didn't believe in astrology, yet had found herself absorbedly checking out the daily forecast for Sagittarius. It was a little unsettling to read that on his birthday, Jon would be "inclined to aggressiveness" and that he "should watch out for conflicts with the opposite sex." As the salesgirl boxed the tweed cap, Kim smiled, thinking she'd have to warn him.

A half-hour later, when she reached the office, she was barely visible behind her armload of packages.

"Got a bathing suit somewhere in there?" Wally called from the city desk.

"Why?" Kim laughed, glancing at the windows, where a surprisingly early snowfall was pasting confetti on the panes. "We due for a heat wave?"

"*You* are. Come here, I'll tell you about it."

It sounded intriguing. One thing Kim loved about her job was never knowing where she would be on a given day. Grabbing up a pencil and a wad of copy paper, she hurried to the city desk.

"Ever been to California?" Wally studied her with his flat greenish eyes.

"That's one place I haven't been. Why?"

"Because that's where you're going." He tossed her a sheaf of publicity handouts. "Publishers' convention. San Francisco. You'll leave Wednesday, come home Saturday night. Nice little junket for you."

It was a long moment before Kim grasped what he was saying, and then the heavy thudding in her chest seemed so noisy she was afraid Wally would hear it too.

She was going with Jon! He had arranged for her to cover his speech! She had to struggle to hide her excitement.

"Of course you know who's one of the banquet speakers?" Wally said.

Kim nodded. She didn't trust her voice to speak sensibly.

"We'll want complete coverage, naturally. Watch to see if he departs from the advance copy of his speech. Oh, yeah, he wants a special interview with that upstate woman publisher, the one who's causing such a stir, organizing some kind of political party. Dumont wants a lively woman's progress story about her."

"Good. She sounds interesting."

"Yeah. I understand she's a looker too." Wally scratched his homely face thoughtfully. "Listen, do a real careful job on this assignment—his speech and everything. Don't mess up, don't treat this lightly."

Kim blinked at him. "Of course I won't. Why do you say that?"

"Never mind. I'm just telling you."

"Please explain. You act as if . . . almost as if you don't think I can handle the assignment."

"Look, let's not get into this. I don't want to say any more."

"I wish you would!"

"I didn't want to upset you, but okay, if you insist. The boss didn't want you for this Frisco deal. He wanted Marge Thompson. I don't know why, but he was dead set against you. I mean, that man was *cold*. Did you do something to make him sore?"

Kim felt the blood drain out of her face. She propped her hands against Wally's desk to support herself.

"I told him Marge Thompson's getting phlebitis shots—she can't come to the office, much less fly to Frisco. I told him you were the only other woman reporter I'd feel confident about. He gave in, but he wasn't happy about it. So watch your step. He's already fired two of my reporters. I don't want to lose you too. Breaking in new reporters ruins my digestion."

Kim looked dazedly at him. "Thanks for the warning."

"Cookie's calling for your plane reservation."

Kim marched to her desk and flung off her typewriter cover, her lips tightly folded. As she struggled to concentrate on a split-page feature that would have to be completed if she were going to Frisco, Wally's words echoed in her ears.

Why would Jon do that, denigrate her to Wally? Wally was her city editor; she needed his good opinion, and she had worked hard to earn it.

Was it possible Jon didn't believe she was up to covering the convention? Did he really think Marge would do a better job?

She glanced resentfully at the door to his office, feeling a wild impulse to fling it open, stamp in, demand an explanation—

And then suddenly all her fury died and she felt immensely foolish.

Of course! Jon was trying to throw people off the trail. Wally . . . the whole office. She should have realized. His request for Marge Thompson was in line with their strategy, the decision to keep their association secret.

Her head cleared and she could actually feel the drop in her pulse rate. She zipped through her feature story, then deftly pounded out her weekly book review. At quitting time she hurried to the reception room to check with Cookie about the plane reservation.

The secretary was snipping dead leaves from her jade plant. Her pots of trailing vines and flowers on the window ledge made a miniature woodland that hid the view of the ugly back alley. "Oh! I thought you were the boss!" Cookie looked nervously toward Jon's closed door. "I wouldn't want him to catch me gardening during working hours."

"I'm sure he wouldn't mind. Your plants give this place its only distinction."

But Cookie, frowning, scurried back to her desk. "Well, you know, after those firings . . ."

"Cookie, those men weren't doing their jobs. You're always on the ball. There wouldn't be a paper without you!"

"Let's hope the feeling is shared by all." Cookie gave a dubious laugh, glancing again in the direction of Jon's office. "Yes, I got you on an afternoon flight." She leaned across the desk and her voice fell to a whisper. "*He*'s leaving earlier. He didn't want you on his flight. Doesn't like to mix with the hoi polloi, I guess."

"Oh, I don't think that's it—" Kim cut off the words.

She couldn't go around defending Jon, but it bothered her, hearing the secretary's not very flattering comments. It wasn't at all like Cookie, talking in an antagonistic way about her employer.

Still, it was a natural reaction. The firings had left everybody a little paranoid. If only she could tell Cookie that Jon had promised her there would be no more dismissals—not now, anyway. If only everyone knew that Jon wasn't the enemy, that he was fighting to save the paper and everyone's job.

He hadn't wanted her on his flight. Even though she knew the reason for Jon's decision, she couldn't help feeling a stab of hurt. It was so silly of her; she and Jon had talked so often about the need to duck gossip-mongers. Just a few nights ago Jon had complained that he was running out of restaurants with private upstairs dining nooks.

"We could let me be the cook, eat at my place now and then," Kim had offered. "Only I'm warning you, I've never mastered anything complicated. My father likes simple foods—very little meat, lots of raw vegetables."

"That's right, you once said you kept house for him."

"Only for a year, the year after Mom died. Then I went to college and Dad took off to do research at Oxford. I suspect he's gotten himself an English girlfriend there. Lately he sounds so . . . so satisfied and happy on the phone."

"Behind that satisfied feeling there always has to be a female?" Jon smiled in an odd way.

"Are you poking fun at me? You think I'm patting myself on the back?"

"You'll never have to do that, not while I'm around.

Nothing I like better than patting your pretty back." He sipped his wine thoughtfully. "No, I was just thinking how you females can affect a man. You just dimple a little and he feels his freedom slipping away and there's not a thing he can do about it."

"Poor, victimized male." Kim smiled teasingly, but still, hadn't she sensed something in his voice . . . just the slightest resentment?

And yet the next moment he was taking her hand. "How could anybody feel poor or victimized sitting next to you? And if he's lucky enough to occupy your bed someday—and you're looking at a man who hopes to reach that exalted state—lady, he would have everything he could ever want."

His words echoed in her mind now as she pulled on her trenchcoat and went down to the lobby. She stepped out onto Broad Street, her feet slipping and sliding in treacherously wet snow as she clutched her armload of packages to her chest.

"Taxi, lady?"

She swiveled her head. Alan Skilton sat at the wheel of a new car, a jaunty silver affair nestled against a No Parking sign. "Alan! What are you doing here? You'll get a ticket!"

"Nice way to greet someone you haven't seen for almost a month. Or has it been a century?" Alan grinned. "Hop in."

"Thanks, but I'm not going home. I'm having dinner with a friend."

"I've got nothing against friends. Let me drop you off. You look as if you've bought out Copley's."

Kim hesitated. She *was* tired, and the snow was just

118

messy enough to ruin her new pumps. "All right, thanks. I'm heading for Rittenhouse Square."

Driving through the slanting curtain of snow, Alan told her that his trip to Chicago had resulted in a new job with a far more promising future. "So I'll be shaking off this town's dust. Might as well. You were the only reason I had to stay around Philly. And even now if you said the word . . ."

"Alan, please. We've gone all over this."

He sighed resignedly. "Okay, I guess I'm licked. Listen, there's one thing—if you don't mind parting with that stereo . . ."

"Of course not. I've always wondered why you didn't come get it."

"The answer's obvious. As long as it was in your place, I had some connection with you. Anyway, all right if I pick it up next week?"

"Any time. And, don't forget to leave the key for me, will you?"

"Sure, but there's one thing I *don't* have to give back."

She looked curiously at him.

"Some darned wonderful memories, Kim."

"You gave me some too, Alan." She placed a quick, light kiss on his jaw, and when he let her out, she turned to wave before sloshing her way into the lobby of Walnut Towers with her armload of packages.

At the penthouse apartment, she almost collided with Jon's maid, who was just rushing out. He had told Kim earlier that Ellie would be there to let her in the apartment.

"Mr. Dumont says he'll be here at eight," Ellie said

in a rush. "Beef casserole's in the oven. He ran out of burgundy so I chilled some champagne. Goodnight!"

Kim smiled her thanks at the hurrying maid and went into the apartment. The telephone rang as she stepped into the foyer and she stood hesitant. She wasn't sure Jon would want her answering his phone. It might be somebody from the office, someone who would recognize her voice. Peering back into the corridor, she called, "Ellie," but the maid's shiny boots were flashing into the elevator.

Kim went back inside and looked at the shrilling phone. Jon, calling to say he'd been delayed?

She plucked up the receiver. "Hello?"

"Hello . . . Ellie? Let me speak to Jon, please."

The voice was youthfully feminine. Kim felt herself stiffening.

"Jon's not here at the moment."

"Oh!" Disappointment coated the word. "This isn't Ellie, is it?"

"Ellie's left. Would you like to leave a message?"

"Oh! Well . . . yes . . . yes. Please tell Jon Amy called. A-m-y."

"Would you care to leave your last name?"

"Oh, he doesn't need that. He'll know who." A little laugh. "You're his new secretary or something?"

"No," Kim said stiffly. "But I'll be sure to give him your message."

"Thank you." The voice was abruptly cooler, and the phone clicked off. Amy had definitely wanted her to be a secretary.

Kim stood with her hand on the phone. Amy . . . She found herself picturing someone with straight

120

blond hair, a pale creamy face. Someone who looked great in riding clothes, a Grace Kelly kind of girl.

She caught sight of her face in the foyer mirror. She looked flushed, strained, her hair disarranged by the snow and wind.

She coaxed it into order and stepped into Jon's huge, silent living room. Tentatively she perched on the edge of the long wraparound suede sofa. She felt oddly intimidated by the apartment, the ticking oriental clock, all the handsome furniture staring at her. Suddenly she felt like an intruder, yet at the same time she was conscious of a terrible desire to roll up her sleeves and methodically poke through the entire place, dig into every corner, rake through every desk and cabinet and closet and drawer, unturn all the secrets of Jon's daily life and make them hers.

It was a disgusting thought, shamefully possessive, not at all typical of her. She'd never felt that way about Alan, never pried into his business.

Her eyes drifted to the pile of packages she'd deposited on the coffee table. Jon would be so pleased with the cap. She couldn't wait to see him try it on.

She got up and tiptoed to the bedroom. She stood looking at the huge bed with its fluffy down coverlet. She remembered lying on it that one night—the down had been so caressing, so conducive to surrender. And she had been so strong and stalwart.

Somehow now the room looked different, or was that because she was alone in it? The huge Mexican sunburst mirror, the shining glass bedside tables topped with oriental lamps, the thick sand-colored carpeting— it all had an alien look. She felt as if the room didn't recognize her, didn't remember she was the girl Jon had once brought to the edge of surrender on that very bed.

One of many girls? Her lips twisted wryly. Naturally he had had other women, an Amy or two lingering on the landscape. Perhaps some of them had gotten to know that down coverlet intimately.

She felt a sudden, immense depression. Telling herself that, after all, *she* was the woman currently featured in his life—or at least she presumed so—she walked quickly back to the dining room, looking for something to occupy her attention. But the table was perfectly set, even to a lily of the valley and yellow rose centerpiece. Ellie had been very conscientious. *The boss is having one of his lady friends in; I've got to be here to open the door for her. No, not Amy, a new one.* Was that what the maid had said tonight, telephoning her boyfriend to explain why she was so late?

Her imaginings were dissolved by the sound of a key turning, footsteps on the entry tiles. The disturbing mood fled as she hurried back to the living room and stationed herself behind the pile of packages on the table. "Ta-ta, ta-taaa," she trumpeted when Jon appeared in the doorway. "I even got the Vatican City stamps Stevie wants!"

Jon smiled. "Oh, great. I never would have had time to track that stuff down, not with the schedule I'm keeping." Shrugging out of his coat, he circled the coffee table. "No cabs anywhere. I walked." He rubbed his cold face against hers.

Snowflakes dotted his hair, like stars in a night sky. She reached up to brush them away. "You look done in."

"I guess we're all in for some rough days in that place."

"But not tonight. This is a very special occasion."

"Of course it is—we're together. And I think I see champagne in that bucket."

He uncorked the bottle and they sat close, thigh touching thigh, and sipped the wine. He put his arm around her and his hand cupped her breast. Kissing the corner of her mouth, he said, "That's better, I'm beginning to feel human again." She patted the roughness of his cheek, where the end-of-the-day beard had surfaced.

"A happy, happy, happy, Jon," she whispered.

He looked blankly at her. "What's the reason for the happy talk?"

"You know." She smiled up at him.

"You mean I have some reason to rejoice other than the obvious one?" He ran a hand along the curve of her thigh.

"Aren't you happy to be on the threshold of another year?"

He continued to look puzzledly at her.

"Happy birthday!" she cried.

His silence startled her. Slowly he sat his wine glass down, centering it precisely on the silver coaster. "That's not until tomorrow," he said in a stiff voice.

"Well, that's close enough for a celebration, isn't it?" She plucked up the package with its flurry of rust-colored ribbon. "Here—happy thirty-fifth!"

He sat looking at the box she had dropped in his lap, but he didn't move to open it. "How in hell did you know?"

She smiled mischievously. "You told me to always check the clips, remember?"

He didn't look at her. "I'm not sure you ought to be doing this . . . giving me presents."

She felt her smile slowly thinning. "This is just a—"

"I never celebrate birthdays." His voice was crisp. "I guess I don't particularly enjoy the thought of time creeping up on me like ivy on a gravestone."

She stared at him. "Well, that's a nice morbid picture. Something to start off the evening with a bang!" She moved her body slightly away from his. "Sorry. I had no intention of depressing you."

"Oh, it's all right. I suppose women have to do this kind of thing—make a ceremony out of something that has meaning only to a child."

"A child?" Kim felt the hurt growing in her throat. "My father said social ceremonies make the difference between us and the beasts. Apes don't celebrate birthdays or anniversaries!" She felt her voice drying up.

There was an awkward silence. He stood up, then abruptly reached down and pulled her up too. "Sorry. I apologize to you and to the honorable institution of birthdays. I guess I felt . . . I suddenly felt as if things were closing in on me."

"Things?" Kim said roughly. "Or *me*?"

He flushed. "Of course not you."

"Please. We said we'd be real—honest—with each other."

He hesitated, then gave a quick nod. "Okay. Just for a moment I felt . . . well, not exactly ready for family-type things like birthday gifts. I guess I don't want things to get too heavy or demanding, not at thirty-five. And blast it, at the same time I realize thirty-five is far from young, and if I ever . . . Well, anyway, I haven't done half of what I hoped to do by this time, and I don't want anything stopping me from doing it!"

"*Summa cum laude* from Princeton, master's from Columbia, an editor on one of the most respected magazines in the country, publisher of a leading paper." Kim's voice was clipped. "What more could you want?"

"You've left out all the negatives. I haven't written anything worth a Pulitzer. I haven't even started the book I plan to write. I haven't made much of a stir in the world."

"You have time," Kim said steadily. "No one's going to get in your way. Certainly not me."

"I didn't mean . . . Look, let's forget what I said. You haven't done anything wrong. I was making a fuss about nothing. You haven't staked any claim on me."

"Of course not," Kim said quickly. "And you haven't on me. That's the way we both want it, I trust."

"Thanks." He looked at her with intent hazel eyes. "It's good we can spell everything out, it's healthy. And now let's see what's in this very handsomely wrapped package."

She watched him draw the cap from the box. Making admiring sounds, he dropped it on his head, peaked the brim, posed haughtily. "Dashing?"

"Very," Kim said evenly.

"It'll go perfectly with a blazer I own."

Yes, your herringbone. She swallowed the words just in time. She couldn't let him feel she was invading his life, poking in his closets, latching onto every part of him.

And she wasn't—and *wouldn't*. She would hate herself if she ever found herself hanging on a man, making him feel caught, cornered.

She reached for her wine glass. As he examined the childrens' gifts and complimented her, a little too vigorously, on each selection, she said casually, "Someone phoned you. I wouldn't have answered, but Ellie wasn't here. This person, Amy, said to tell you she called."

"Thanks." His eyes stayed flat, unrevealing, but his body tensed slightly, as if expecting questions, a quiz about Amy.

"I'll check the casserole." She dove into the kitchen, desperately needing to be away from him for a while. She felt spun about, confused, somehow even a little sad.

Then he was coming swiftly after her, and when her arms went out to hold him back, he pinned them down, bringing his body close against hers. "I hope you know I want us both to be happy. I want us to be like that day at Cape May, light as thistledown."

Kim stared into his eyes. Was he telling her that this was a bubble of a romance, one that could last only while it floated, one that would quickly die if it came up against something solid? She couldn't read his face, but she felt his body, felt the desire tensing his loins. Folding her lips, she pushed away from him. "If you really want me to be happy," she said brightly, "I'll tell you how to start."

"How's that?" He was speaking absently now, suddenly occupied with looking at her, his eyes taking on a hazy sheen of desire as they moved from her clinging blouse to her flaring jersey skirt.

"Well, for one thing"—darting around him before his touch could weaken her, she reached for a potholder—"you can stop cutting me down."

"Cutting you down?"

"When you talk to Wally. He *is* my editor, you know."

He didn't reply, and very deliberately she didn't look at him. Taking the casserole from the oven she said coolly, "You toss the salad."

"I didn't cut you down." Obediently he lifted the salad bowl. "I simply asked Wally to assign Marge Thompson instead of you."

"That's cutting me down! I know you did it so Wally wouldn't think there was anything between us, but . . ."

"I didn't do it for that reason. I just didn't want you in Frisco."

She whirled to stare open-mouthed at him. "Well, thanks! I certainly wouldn't want to intrude! You're privileged to feel any way you wish about my company. But you're *not* privileged to imply to Wally that I can't handle an assignment! It took me a long time to prove myself to that man. I don't want him getting any notion that maybe he made a mistake!"

"I hardly think there's any danger of that."

"You can't believe it improves my professional status to have you, the publisher, announce you don't want me covering your speech?"

His shoulders moved restlessly. "I can't help that. I would prefer not to have you there."

"Tell me why not. You owe me that!"

He sighed impatiently. "All right. But look, don't take this personally. It's just that going out of town with

127

you, putting up in the same hotel . . . you let your professionalism slip for one minute in front of a group like that, other publishers . . . can't you see what it would do to me? It's just too risky. You must understand that." He gave a smile obviously meant to soothe her, then put his arm around her shoulder.

Kim felt the anger rising in her throat. She crossed her arms in front of her, making a barrier. So it hadn't been an act. He really didn't want her to go with him. The thought was humiliating. She was glad Marge Thompson was out of commission, glad he would have to endure her presence.

"I think you'd better get one thing straight," she said coldly. "I'm a newspaper reporter. Knowing you hasn't changed that. And traveling with you won't either. I guarantee I'll still perform my job competently. And I want to tell you something—you talk about wanting a Pulitzer. You think you're the only one? I happen to have a few ambitions myself! And I can assure you that when I land in San Francisco, I'll be strictly a working reporter. You won't find me hanging on your arm like . . . like some overloaded camera case! You insult me! I couldn't believe it when I heard you didn't want me on the same plane! I mean, really! I wouldn't try to sit on your lap!"

"I never thought you would. Actually, I arranged for the earlier flight because I have a number of papers to look over."

"And you were afraid I'd turn all pouty and put out because you weren't gazing into my limpid eyes?" Kim shook her head. "You don't know me very well, do you?"

"Not nearly well enough. But I do know myself." He

half turned from her, and his voice lowered. "I know being in an out-of-town hotel with you . . . I'll have a rough time concentrating on my work."

"I've never once interfered with your work!"

He didn't seem to hear. "It's going to be very difficult." His eyes met hers almost beseechingly, but she felt herself hardening. *Men.* They expected instant understanding, capitulation even in their most unreasonable moods, she thought bitterly. But they rarely gave that kind of response to women.

She swerved away from him, her heels clicking as she moved to the far side of the gleaming white-tiled kitchen. "Look, my father is a pretty wise man. He brought me up to take care of myself. He saw how the world was headed, how women would have to be able to stand on their own, not be bowled over by life, or men, or anything. I can function on more than one level, just the way you can. So relax—I'll never hang on you. Because when I start doing that, I lose my own sovereignty!"

He looked across the room at her, a little smile playing at his lips.

"Don't laugh!" she cried fiercely. "I mean every word of it!"

"I see that you do. And suddenly I realize how wonderful you are, how spirited and rare. Forgive me for being so slow to see that. Okay, San Francisco— open your Golden Gate!"

In three long strides he was at her side and this time she couldn't pull away. His arms swept her to him, and as he kissed her she felt her mouth soften, ripen and turn as fervent and searching as his.

Standing close to him, she found herself wondering if

what she had said was true. *Could* she love a man this much and yet not want to own him? Could she compartmentalize her life, keep part of herself whole and thriving despite her body's increasing desire for him?

I can handle it, I know I can, she told herself. But then she remembered him saying he wanted to keep things light. He was even afraid of being alone with her in an out-of-town hotel. Wasn't that, too, part of a wish to avoid real involvement?

Now, feeling his hands fall from her, seeing him make a bowing movement in the direction of the dining room table, she gave him a quick, curious glance. Was there something new in his manner, something remote from the passion of a few days ago? Here they were, far from everyone, screened off, alone in a snow-muted world, and just a few feet away the bedroom waited, with its low lights and sensuously soft coverlet. . . .

Yet he was making no move to lure her to his bed.

You idiot, she told herself, he's taking you at your word. Yet, looking at him over the floral centerpiece, Kim felt her heart lurch with sudden pain.

Perhaps Jon had decided the better part of wisdom was to stop wanting to make love to her.

Chapter Nine

"Ladies and gentleman, we are three and a half hours into our flight and right on the button," the pilot's lazily confident voice said on the 747's intercom.

Kim sipped the last of her cocktail and opened her notebook. Idly she began to sketch the interesting-looking woman across the aisle.

Kim had always enjoyed sketching. It was a relaxing hobby. A few of her illustrations had actually been used in the *Recorder* when there were no photos to brighten a story.

Covertly she studied her present subject. *Striking, strong, expensive*—those words came to mind. The woman had chiseled features, expertly designed hair. Her eyelashes were thick as fur. Her clothes were investment quality: fine silk shirt, great-looking suede pants, marvelous angora sweater-coat. Lots of bronze bracelets and matching bronze fingernails.

Hard-edged as a diamond, Kim decided, sketching the lady's jutting chin. She was obviously a career woman. Kim could see the mandatory fine leather briefcase and piles of important-looking papers. A buyer? A top-flight decorator? Maybe a bank executive?

Whatever the lady was, just looking at all that pristine perfection made Kim feel hopelessly disheveled. Irritable with herself, she dropped her pencil and headed back to the powder room. Wally *would* pick the day of her flight to send her out to a five-alarm fire! She'd had to walk around fire hoses, duck sprays and ladders and charred messes. There were mud stains on her good rose wool suit. And then the mad scramble to reach the airport—she hadn't had time for a sandwich, much less a few minutes to fool with her eye shadow.

And why had she decided at the last minute to style her hair with jagged bangs? Suppose Jon didn't like such a severe look? Not that he was likely to comment one way or another. In the elevator this morning he had obviously been intent on setting the tone for their stay in San Francisco. His "Good morning, Miss Curtis" had had all the intimacy of a metronome, even though there was no one from the office sharing their elevator.

She glanced at her watch. By now, with his earlier flight, Jon was comfortably settled in San Francisco. Well, he wouldn't have to worry. She wouldn't embarrass him when they met, wouldn't show by even a flicker of an eyelash that they were anything more than boss and employee.

Walking down the aisle, her eye was caught by a flash of lightning from a window. She paused to stare out at the grey, moiling vista.

"All squared away?"

The deep voice was so close that she turned, thinking the man was addressing her, but then she saw that his face was turned toward a woman standing at the magazine rack.

It was Miss Super Achiever herself, the lady with the bronze fingernails.

Kim's eyes went back to the man. She had run into him somewhere before. She remembered those eyes. They had a wild fixed look that didn't match the rest of his urbane appearance. He was tall, thin, grey-haired and immaculately dressed.

"The big point for you to remember," he was saying softly to the woman, "is to always stress that this is strictly a grass-roots operation. Your support comes from humble country people. Stick to that and you're okay."

"Haven't we gone all over this a dozen times before? Do you take me for a fool?" The woman's voice was edgy. "Oh, come on, darling, let's relax and get ourselves a drink!"

The man shook his head. "Better not be seen too cosy together. We agreed that's best, remember?"

The words put a grim smile on Kim's lips. Was every boss in the world worried about being caught in an unholy alliance with some woman employee?

Back in her seat she picked up her notebook and found herself sketching her vivid recollection of the man's peculiar eyes—hazy, staring, as if behind them lived some bizarre fantasy. She drew the long thin face, the grooved forehead, the narrow lips that looked as if they could turn nasty very quickly.

Miss Super Achiever slid back into her seat, calling to the flight attendant for a Scotch and soda. The woman began to jot notes while she waited. One of those tireless, driving women, Kim thought, laden with a million nagging desires.

And in love with Mr. Wild Eyes? Kim wondered idly. Where *had* she seen that man before? Impossible to remember. A reporter ran into dozens of people in the course of a day; hundreds, in the course of a week.

Putting her head back, she closed her eyes, suddenly feeling the long day catch up with her.

She woke to hear the pilot announcing that San Francisco was down there waiting for them.

Across the aisle Miss Super Achiever was ready, sitting bolt upright, every hair in place, her expression proclaiming her intention to be the first to storm the Golden Gate.

Kim, gathering up her things, caught the view from the window and blinked in dismay.

"I thought it never rained in San Francisco!" she gasped at her cab driver a half-hour later. She had found a cab only because of her willingness to run through the deluge to catch it.

"Lady, that's not rain," he said with a straight face. "Anybody in San Francisco will tell you that's just a little mist."

Kim didn't answer. She didn't want to quash anybody's civic pride. But her first fifteen minutes in this city had turned her bangs into frizz.

She was even more conscious of her frazzled appearance when she entered the lobby of her hotel and caught a blurred impression of magnificence: redwood burl panels, crystal chandeliers, luxurious brocaded chairs under glowing oil paintings.

Luckily it was midafternoon in California and the lobby was practically empty. Some male voices drifted from the bar, but in a few minutes, Kim told herself, she'd be in her room, free to make repairs on her appearance.

"A single? Absolutely not! I requested a suite and that's precisely what I expect!"

She wasn't surprised to see that the voice belonged to Miss Super Achiever, her bronze fingernails tapping out annoyance on the room clerk's counter.

"So sorry, madam"—the clerk flipped the pages of his book—"I can't locate your name on our reservation list."

"That's not my concern. The reservation was made. Look again. Rachel Moran, publisher of the *Allenby Provider.*"

Kim felt herself staring. Rachel Moran. This was the publisher she was scheduled to interview? It didn't seem possible—this sleek, power-hungry type working on a small-town weekly.

"Oh, you're with the publishers!" The clerk was red-faced. "We do have your name, but someone spelled it incorrectly. Horan instead of Moran. I do apologize!"

"Have room service send me the wine list immediately." Rachel Moran slapped out the words. "Oh, and give me Mr. Dumont's room number."

"Mr. Dumont? Here he is, madam, coming from the bar."

Kim felt the jolt of her heart. Turning, she saw Jon striding toward them. He wore a suit she didn't recognize, an elegant charcoal pinstripe, the kind of suit handsome Londoners wore strolling along Bond Street.

"Ah, Miss Moran, I could say I recognize you from your photos," Jon said smoothly. "Except that your photos are a grave miscarriage of justice." He bowed slightly, his smile crinkling the skin around his eyes—and at the same moment he caught sight of Kim.

She simply wanted to die. The exquisite, many-tiered chandelier over her head was a heartless spotlight that must have clearly shown her in all her stained and rumpled glory.

In that moment Kim—who had always told herself that while appearances mattered, they weren't a top priority—suddenly knew that when it came to Jon, her philosophical attitudes underwent some peculiar changes. She couldn't help it—she wanted to look great when his eyes were on her.

"Well!" His hand touched her elbow, steered her closer to Rachel. "This is a fortunate meeting. Miss Moran, this is my capable writer, Miss Curtis." His eyes swept Kim, their expression impersonal. "Miss Curtis is the young lady who will be doing your interview."

"Wonderful!" Rachel's gaze flicked swiftly and diminishingly over Kim, then rushed warmly back to Jon. "Look, why don't we three get together now, when there's no convention business? After we've had time to tidy up, of course." The dark eyes swept back to Kim. "Suppose we meet at cocktail hour in my suite, 1042. I promise to provide champagne. After all, Mr. Dumont, I owe it to you! I'm so honored the *Recorder* wants to interview me. I've admired your paper for eons!"

"And I've been admiring your work," Jon said. "You've caused quite a stir upstate, Miss Moran. In fact, I had planned to send a reporter up to interview you and then I learned you'd be at this convention."

Kim glanced at him. Obviously he was impressed by Rachel's sleekness. Oh, men could be so irritatingly superficial!

They headed for the elevator, Kim deliberately trailing behind. She couldn't help noticing that Rachel held her body quite close to Jon's, and as he talked, her eyes stayed fixed on his face almost prayerfully. A passerby, seeing them, might assume they were either longtime friends or devoted lovers. And Kim, following in their wake, felt as if she were the baggage.

In the next hour she showered and restyled her hair. She did a little overtime with her blusher. In an elegant room like this one, she felt an obligation to look her best. The walls were covered in peach brocade, the long windows draped in a coppery velvet. The tables were marble-topped and delicate and the chairs had puffy down cushions. A bud vase on the dresser held a single peach-tinged rose and there was a copy of the morning paper atop the gold and white escritoire.

She had packed an afternoon dress, a sedate beige silk. She looked at it, then promptly stashed it away in her closet and took out her violet harem pants and mauve shirt. Something told her Rachel Moran wouldn't be wearing anything sedate, not the way that woman walked when she was with a man.

She feels obliged to conquer every male in sight, Kim thought, her nose wrinkling in distaste. It's part of her tool kit, her blueprint for success. Rachel's approach had certainly worked with Jon—he had looked at her so intently.

Kim promptly scolded herself for the thought. Jon was a newsman. He looked intently at millions of things—giraffes and raindrops and mailboxes and the expressions on people's faces. It was the way a newsman was made.

Curious, she thought, that a woman like Rachel would be content to run an unimportant paper like the *Allenby Provider* and to live in bleak, coal-mine country. Hard to picture her in an ink-stained cubbyhole, sharing space with some worndown linotype machines.

Lately, though, Rachel had been more and more in the spotlight. The *Provider* was calling for the formation of a new political party, and people were taking the proposal seriously, contributing funds even though the new party's platform hadn't been spelled out yet.

Something flickered distantly and disturbingly in Kim's mind. Plucking up her notebook, she studied the sketch she had made of the man on the plane, Rachel's friend who hadn't wanted to be seen with her, but it was no use. She hadn't the faintest idea of where she had run into him.

Dropping the notebook, she turned back to make a final check in the mirror. The girl in the harem pants, she decided, would pass muster.

But her nervousness returned a few minutes later when she knocked on Rachel's door. She could hear the faint echo of Jon's voice. He certainly hadn't lost any time getting here, she thought, and knocked again.

Rachel threw open the door. "I'm afraid you've got

the wrong—" She blinked. "Oh, Miss Curtis—sorry! Your hair . . . you look completely different!"

"I got a little bored with the drowned-rat look." Kim smiled a polite employee's smile at Jon, comfortably ensconced on the sofa with a champagne glass. She sat in the chair farthest from him, and looked around the suite. Rachel had treated herself to the best. Her sitting room was enormous, and beyond it lay an even larger, ivory-walled bedroom.

And atop the bed, well-lighted by a tall red lacquer lamp, Kim saw a froth of black lace, a nightgown spread out enticingly.

And deliberately? Kim's lips folded. She suspected Rachel rarely did anything accidental.

"You look sweet, dear, that wonderful scrubbed look. So healthy!" Rachel handed her a glass of champagne. Kim saw she had gone all-out with her appearance. Rachel wore a black chiffon caftan, and only a black lace half-slip under it. In the lamplight Rachel's nipples prodded the caftan brazenly.

"Yes, you do look charming this evening, Miss Curtis," Jon said dutifully.

As contrasted with this afternoon? Kim thought sourly. But she thanked him in a cool, easy voice.

"Despite her pretty little outfit, she's ready to work!" Rachel purred. "I see you've brought your notebook."

"I also say my prayers every night and eat carrots to curl my hair," Kim said.

Jon looked quickly at her, but Rachel was either unaware of the sarcasm or didn't wish to notice. "Isn't this delicious champagne?" she chattered. "Who says Paris is the only place to get good wine? This is a local product, I'm glad to say. I always promote American-made products. It's one of the things we stress in our editorials in the *Provider*."

"By the way," Jon said, "do you write those editorials yourself? Some of them are real powderkegs." He leaned toward Rachel, like a pointer catching a scent, Kim thought, a very seductive scent.

"Every word comes straight from my own private little brain cells, Mr. Dumont." Now Rachel was leaning toward him. Kim saw the exchange of glances, glances that lingered just a little too long.

"This new political party you're calling for," Jon went on, "you have any important people interested?"

Rachel smiled serenely. "The most important person in the country: Mr. Average American. It's so gratifying! He's sending us his dimes and quarters. Obviously he agrees we need new grass-roots leadership." Rachel raised a hand to her sleek hair and Kim caught the glitter of an impressive star sapphire.

She's a schemer, pure and simple, Kim thought. She's not interested in grass-roots people or grass-roots anything.

Or had her judgment been affected by the blatant way Rachel was making a play for Jon?

"Well, what we want from you, Rachel, is an in-depth interview," Jon said. "I figure that'll take at least two hours of your time, so perhaps I should leave you and Miss Curtis alone now, and let you get right down to work?"

Instantly Rachel's hand went out, the bronze-tipped fingers encircling Jon's wrist. "I'll agree to that, but only on one condition—that you come back in precisely two hours and feed this starving female. I'm yearning to experience the French Room . . . I've heard all about their sweetbreads Periquex. Will you, kind sir, be my escort for the evening?"

"That sounds very appealing." Jon stood up.

Still holding onto his wrist, Rachel stood up too, her body swaying seductively close. Beseechingly she raised his captured hand to her cheek in a dramatic, utterly graceful gesture. "For me it will be the highlight of the convention, to spend time with someone I've so long admired!"

What a clever maneuver, Kim thought. She's managed to get Jon to herself for the evening simply by pretending there's no one else in the room.

"I can't imagine a more charming introduction to a business parley." Jon disengaged his hand from Rachel's, but his eyes were smiling.

Oh, he can be so devilishly cool and smooth, Kim thought, with sick admiration. No one would ever guess he has any connection with me, that I've seen him with tousled hair and the dazed look of passion on his face.

Suddenly she almost didn't believe it herself. She felt as if she had fantasized the past weeks and all that had gone on between her and Jon Dumont.

Miserably she watched him move to the door, forced herself to match his departing smile.

Then he was gone and Rachel was sitting down again, crossing her slim legs. "Simply charming man! If a woman has to work for someone, it might as well be that kind of someone! I adore his cologne. I wonder what brand it is?"

"Aramis," Kim heard herself blurt defiantly.

Immediately shame flooded her. She was betraying Jon, doing precisely what she had sworn not to do.

Under Rachel's abruptly sharpened scrutiny, she felt her cheeks burning. How could she be so absurd? Showing off, hinting that she had more than a business connection with the boss.

It was unforgivable, yet she realized that the impulse behind her remark had been a primitive one, impossible to resist.

Saying that one revelatory word had been like an animal baring its teeth, an animal that sensed the presence of a life-threatening enemy.

Later, sitting alone at an elegantly appointed table in the French Room, Kim tried to look unaware of Jon and Rachel, dining a half-dozen tables away. She was relieved when her view of them was cut off as the room filled with people as beautiful to look at as the spectacular furnishings. Many of the men wore black tie, and the ladies long gowns; here among the antique sideboards and oil paintings, formal dress seemed mandatory.

The food matched the surroundings, Kim thought, sampling the Spanish shrimp royale simmered in champagne sauce. A bevy of waiters seemed intent on anticipating her every need. As soon as she reached for the silver coffeepot, someone appeared to pour for her. Not a crumb was permitted to linger more than a few seconds on the damask tablecloth.

All in all, she told herself, there was no sensible reason not to be enjoying herself. She knew she looked attractive; a man at a nearby table gazed appreciatively at her as she stood up to leave. And her interview with Rachel had gone smoothly. The woman had been more open than Kim had expected, admitting she had been helped along by a fortuitous set of circumstances. A wealthy uncle had left her the *Provider* in addition to a "fairly generous" lifetime allowance. "And very luckily," Rachel had smilingly confessed, "because frankly, I simply *adore* luxury."

Why did Kim have the feeling Rachel's free and easy revelations were in themselves a pretense, that Rachel seemed to be saying See how honest I am?

There's something ruthless and conniving about her, Kim decided, something almost too clever.

She wondered what Jon's reaction was. But how could any man make an objective judgment when sitting opposite a woman dressed in an almost transparent gown? And a woman like Rachel, with her obvious drive for power, might hold a special appeal for a man like Jon, who had a super-charged drive himself.

Heading back to her room, she tried to laugh off the memory of Rachel's black nightgown spread so invitingly on her bed. Anything so unsubtle would have to have been unintentional.

As she inserted the key in her door, she heard the phone ringing.

She almost threw herself across the room to reach it.

Hearing Jon's voice, rich, deep, reassuringly warm, made all her doubts wither. Lying back on her bed, cradling the receiver, she cried recklessly; "I *hated* seeing you over there in that dining room! I almost threw my rolls at you!"

"I wasn't exactly thrilled by all that space between us, either, but she wanted to talk politics. What kind of interview did you get? Rachel says you're charming, by the way."

Yes, she would say that, clever lady, Kim thought.

"The interview was fine," she said briskly. She didn't want to talk about Rachel or the interview. Couldn't he sense that?

"We'll talk over your story angle at lunch tomorrow," he said.

"Why not now?" Kim said brashly. "Over a brandy in the bar. I promise to wear a very businesslike expression, so nobody will think we're doing something naughty, like enjoying ourselves."

He didn't laugh—in fact, didn't respond at all. Kim waited, hearing her quickened heartbeats. I'm such a fraud, she thought. I want him here, in this room. I want him touching me.

He cleared his throat. "Sorry, but I promised Rachel I'd take her across the Golden Gate Bridge. She's never been and . . ."

Kim had to restrain herself from telling him that she'd never been there either. "By all means do that." She made her voice calm, nonchallenging. "I hope I have time to see it too."

"The program leaves everybody free to sightsee tomorrow afternoon."

"Thanks for letting me know." She hadn't wanted the sudden sharpness that had crept into her voice, the anger that was churning in her all at once. "While you're escorting your friend around, I'd advise you to keep your ears open. The woman's a shark!"

"What? What the devil do you mean?"

The harsh edge of his voice made her falter. "I . . . it's just an intuitive feeling."

"Since when does a reporter regard intuition as fact?"

144

"Oh . . . oh, never mind!" Kim astounded herself by slamming the phone down.

And then she sat very still, her pulses racing. If only she could take it all back, every disgusting jealous word! She felt diseased, jealousy twisting in her insides, corrosive and ugly.

She had no valid reason to make accusations against Rachel Moran. Even the conversation on the plane didn't mean anything special. The wild-eyed man could have been advising Rachel what to say in her interview with the *Recorder*. If he were Rachel's lawyer or business partner, or simply an old friend, there was no reason why he shouldn't advise her.

No, the truth was that she wanted there to be something sinister about Rachel because of the way she was acting with Jon. In all probability Rachel wasn't actually interested in him, but was just playing politics, using her attractiveness to ensure favorable publicity in the *Recorder*.

Wearily Kim began to undress. The maid had drawn down the covers and left two chocolate mints and a small card atop the plump pillow. "Pleasant dreams," the card said. It was an unexpected and soothing touch, designed to make a person feel like a valued guest, not just the occupant of Room 740.

But although she ate the mints, no pleasant dreams awaited her. Instead she lay staring bleakly out at a rainless sky and a moon that looked like a stage prop, perfectly shaped and cut from glistening gold foil.

Once again she remembered Rachel posing near the table lamp, standing so that Jon could see the outline of her unrestrained breasts under the caftan. Once again she saw Rachel raising Jon's hand to her cheek.

She *is* a shark, Kim thought miserably, I know she is.

She lay awake for a long time, dreading the arrival of the next day. She had the feeling that when she saw Rachel's face again she would instantly be able to tell if she and Jon had done more than cross a bridge on this lovely night, under this golden San Francisco moon.

Chapter Ten

Sunlight sparkled on the crystal and silver as Kim entered the Burgundy Room for the breakfast that preceded the convention's opening session.

Seating herself at Table No. 9, she saw in one swift glance that Jon's place card was at her left, and that Rachel Moran was seated three satisfying tables away.

From under lowered eyelids she surveyed Rachel. The woman wore an elegant black knit dress and the ruby-red choker around her neck seemed almost to sizzle. Did Rachel's face have a new glow, or was it just very expertly applied blusher?

"Good morning."

Kim felt the jolt of her heart as Jon pulled out a chair and sat down beside her.

"I'm sorry about what I said last night." She got the

words out in a hurry, her skin burning. "I was completely out of line."

"Forget it," he said crisply. "Enjoy your breakfast."

Feeling miserable, she picked up her orange juice.

A man at her right breezily introduced himself: Clint Warren, from a South Carolina newspaper. "And who are you?" he said.

Kim explained that she wasn't a publisher, just a reporter, and she worked for the man on her left, who was . . .

"Oh, I already know Dumont. I'm interested in knowing about *you*." Clint gave a lighthearted laugh. "Didn't know they grew girl reporters like you. You must be a brand new variety on the market."

"Hey, Warren," Jon intervened, "don't risk calling my reporter a girl. She'll whip out her machete before you can say sorry."

"I left my machete home this trip." Kim laughed.

"I don't get your meaning, Dumont. She looks like a girl, smells like a girl." Clint Warren ran a hand lightly over the back of Kim's hair. *"Feels* like a girl. Yes, sir, I suspect this is honest-to-goodness girl."

Kim laughed again. She understood men like Clint. Those full lips and heavily lashed eyes, the elfin face—she had come to associate that look with playful, innocent Don Juans; harmless, boyish men who made a game of flirting with any woman in their vicinity.

"You Northerners just don't know how to handle the ladies. See how they respond to some plain old Southern charm?" Clint beamed around the table, then turned attentively back to Kim. "Honey, let's you and me go get us some bourbon to liven up this orange juice. We're too young and vibrant for all this dreary business palaver."

"Thanks." Kim laughed. "But I can be vibrant without bourbon, particularly at breakfast."

"Honey, I'll bet you can!" Clint passed her a silver dish of grilled sausages. "Listen, if you ever want to migrate to South Carolina, look me up. I could use a reporter with gorgeous blue eyes. There's a real shortage of them."

Kim felt deliciously, almost perversely happy because Jon's mouth was twitching slightly, the way it did when he was annoyed and didn't want to show it.

But at that point the chairman rapped his gavel and she riveted her attention on the opening session.

The subject was "Metropolitan Newspapers—An Endangered Species?" The speaker drew some dismaying conclusions and she and Jon exchanged somber glances.

It was a heavy conference, lasting well past noon. As Kim hurried to the elevator to wash up for lunch, she caught sight of something glittery at the end of the lobby.

It was Rachel's stunning garnet choker, catching the light from the huge chandeliers. Rachel's smile was a matching dazzle as she looked up at Jon and fingered his lapel.

Kim turned her eyes away and kept going. In the elevator she intently studied an advertisement for the hotel's various dining facilities. Just as the doors started to close, Jon and Rachel pushed in. "Ten!" Rachel called imperiously, as if there were an elevator operator. Immediately, one of the passengers darted a hand to the button, moving as if activated by radar. Did Rachel get instant service every time she opened her mouth? Kim wondered sourly.

She studied the back of Jon's head, wondering if he was getting off at Rachel's floor. There was no way to find out, since Kim's floor was seven and Jon's was nine.

Unless she stayed aboard and spied, which she would certainly never do. But she had to admit she was tempted.

The knowledge filled her with a plunging sense of gloom. The feeling stayed with her all the way through the luncheon. The speaker was terribly dull, and playful Clint Warren wasn't around to enliven things. For some reason he was seated at Table No. 21, far across the room.

She glanced at Jon. He was completely absorbed, taking down endless statistics on the cost of newsprint. When the ice cream dishes were cleared away and the speaker had droned his final word, Jon turned to her. "You said your interview with Rachel went off fairly well. When you work out your lead, I'd like to see it."

"I intend to start writing as soon as there's a free minute."

"I'm sure it will be a colorful piece. Rachel's an interesting woman. I was surprised last night, when you said what you did on the phone."

Kim put her spoon down carefully. "Appraising a person is always subjective. I just didn't warm to the lady as much as you did. I have this nagging feeling she's not quite fourteen carat; you haven't sensed anything like that?"

There, Kim told herself, that came across calmly.

But his eyes, looking at her, were coolly speculative. "The feeling I have is that you can't handle this, Kim."

"Handle what?"

"This whole situation. You can't separate our emotional connection from our business association. You obviously resent the fact that I have to deal with other people, in this case another woman."

"You didn't have to deal with her last night!"

The words came from nowhere, the awful, humiliating words.

His lips flickered. "I knew you were resentful that I wasn't able to be with you. I considered phoning you when I got back, which, by the way, was quite early. But I decided to wait till you calmed down. Truthfully, I was shocked that you were so needlessly jealous."

"I wasn't! That's insulting!" Kim said.

But as she stared at him, her eyes tracing the familiar curve of his lips, she felt a huge disappointment in herself welling up, filling her. It was her fault. She was spoiling what she so wanted to be an honest, superior relationship. She just had to get herself in hand.

"Excuse me!" She clambered up, awkwardly juggling her purse and notebook.

"Where are you going? Kim—"

His arm went out to halt her, but she avoided his grasp, and swept past the sound of buzzing voices and clattering silver. She fixed her eyes straight ahead, holding her mouth tight so it wouldn't tremble.

She had to be by herself, look sternly at herself. Her feelings about Jon were turning her into a baffling, terrifying stranger, and she wasn't going to allow it.

Yes, she needed Jon's love, but she needed her self-respect every bit as much.

She had always been a walker and now, shaking off the hothouse atmosphere of the hotel, she flung herself into a brilliant afternoon with white clouds drifting dreamily against a Wedgewood sky.

Circling Union Square's palm trees and elegant shops, she felt herself gradually quieting down, and as she wandered into a less formal section of the city, she began to enjoy the up and down streets, the alleys and nooks, the tiny courtyards crammed with serendipities. Live parrots wearing name tags around their necks made a jungle of one store window. In Galahad's Beauty Shop a manicurist sat in the window, painting astrological signs on a customer's fingernails. On the corner a gnarled man composed poems to order. Five dollars per sonnet; ten if you wanted one printed on parchment.

Going down a steep hill, Kim gasped in surprise at a sweeping row of lacy Victorian houses, all done up in jelly bean pastels; they looked like court ladies parading their fancy gowns.

A young woman stood on the front steps of a particularly lovely structure with lavender gingerbread. Shading her eyes, she peered down the street. She looked vibrant and happy, as if waiting for the man she loved.

Watching her, Kim felt a return of hopelessness. Jon and I are not going to work out, she thought. At once her whole being violently rebelled. No, I won't let it go! I won't lose what it's been, this brimming treasure.

"Things can't be all that bad, honey."

She turned dazedly. Clint Warren was standing behind her. "Are you following me?" she said sharply. She didn't want to talk to anyone at the moment.

"If you want a straight answer, yes." He grinned. "You said you might join me on sightseeing day, remember?"

Kim looked blankly at him. He wore jeans and a casual sweater, and a camera was slung over his shoulder. Sightseeing . . . yes, Jon had said it was on the day's program. And where was *he* at the moment? Walking on Fisherman's Wharf with Rachel? Taking her to Muir Woods, standing close to her under the awesome redwoods?

"Hey, you look as if someone just told you there'll be no tomorrow. Come on, give me a sample of that pretty smile. Make the boys at the plant jealous." Clint slid his camera off his shoulder.

"Well . . ." Kim struggled to smile accommodatingly.

After that they headed down the hill. She was aware that Clint was talking. Now and then she made vague answering sounds.

And somehow, sometime after that, she found herself seated in the bar at the Top of the Mark. The view of the brilliant jumble of San Francisco abruptly stirred her to life. "Oh, this city is so marvelous, so vibrant," she said.

"There, now you sound more like yourself. What's been eating you, darlin'?" Clint said. "You rushed out at lunch looking as if that high-powered boss of yours stamped on all ten of your toes."

"I'd rather not talk about it, Clint."

"Yeah, I can see he'd be a headache to work for, tough as buffalo hide. The way he talked in the bar the other day . . . that man's on a march to glory, and you people on that paper are just ducks in a shooting gallery."

"Why do you say that?"

Clint shrugged. "I got the impression he's set to make a wholesale sweep of personnel. No room for failures with that man. When you're down, honey, you're out!"

"Well, you're wrong. Mr. Dumont's not planning any firings. I happen to know," Kim said. Suddenly she couldn't think about Jon for another moment. She looked around frantically for something to distract her. "Clint, what building is that, the one with the marvelous rooftop garden?"

But Clint wasn't obtuse. "Okay, okay—I won't say another nasty word about your dynamite boss. It's always the ones with the Adonis profiles who get away with murder, isn't it?"

The sky was a deep violet tinged with orange and her phone was shrilling when Kim got back to her room.

She turned on the lamps, and let the phone continue to shrill. Which it did, intermittently for the next hour and a half, while she sat at her typewriter, fingers flying.

Lights were strung like crown jewels along the distant bridge when her hands finally fell from the keyboard.

She felt strangely quiet and at peace with herself

when she picked up the phone and dialed Jon's room number.

"I've been phoning you all afternoon," he said. "Where the devil have you been?"

She closed her eyes. "I'm here now, Jon," she said mildly. She was tired of arguments. "I'd like to talk to you."

"I'm coming right down."

The phone clicked dead. And now abruptly her calm was shattered. She hadn't expected him to come to her room, not after all his talk about keeping a cautious distance between them. But maybe the intimacy of her bedroom wouldn't touch him. Maybe he could sit in the soft light, even drop down on the bed, and not think of the times he had caressed her.

Quickly she moved around, turning on all the lights. But she couldn't seem to diminish the glowing, sensual ambience of the luxurious room.

She waited, the typed sheets of her interview with Rachel stacked at her elbow. When she let him into the room, he made a movement as if to touch her, but she edged away quickly.

"Jon, I've just finished writing Rachel's interview."

"So that's what you've been up to! Great." He reached expectantly for the manuscript.

"Jon, I want to tell you"—she kept her voice steady —"this was a terrible experience for me, the hardest assignment I've ever had."

"What do you mean? It's just a routine feature."

She nodded. "I know. But I really had to struggle to do it fairly, impartially. You see, you were right about my being jealous. I've thought and thought about it, and I realize for the first time that my personal feelings are affecting my reportorial ability. That's something I can't have happen, I can't let my career fall apart. So"—she pulled in her breath—"I've decided that the best thing to do is to either leave the paper"—her voice cracked just a little—"or break up with you."

Chapter Eleven

"What the hell are you talking about?" With one long step Jon closed the gap between them, yanking her to him. Abruptly his mouth clamped down on hers. In an instant everything she had been thinking—all the careful sensible words she had planned to say—turned into puffs of smoke. Her breasts, crushed against the hard armor of his body, tingled unbearably. "Jon!" she mumbled, but his lips were owning her, moving in a hot path across her cheek to her earlobe and on to the shiveringly delicate corridor behind her ear. His tongue teased, lit a fire there, and all her nerve endings shrieked like demons.

Gasping, she tried to pull away, but at the same time her fingers were embarking on their own perverse venture, digging into his shoulders, striving to bring him even closer, and she felt her hips clinging magnetically to his taut hardness. As if from across miles, she heard his voice hoarsely saying her name, and then, holding her so tightly that he almost cut off her breathing, he swept her to the bed.

"No!" she managed to gasp. "No, Jon!"

His movements stilled as he gazed at her with glittering eyes. "What do you mean—no?" His mouth looked swollen, ready to consume her.

"I can't—we've got to talk!"

"Talk?" His lips writhed around the word.

"About things . . . us! It's not going right with us."

Roughly he pushed her down on the bed. Lowering his body over hers, his hand darted under her blouse, hungrily seeking her breasts.

"I mean it, Jon!" She twisted painfully away. "It's important!"

"Oh, my God, woman, do you know what you're doing to me?" He ran a hand over his forehead and slowly sat up. The flush of passion had left a winey stain on his cheeks.

"Jon . . ." she struggled, "I think we're going in the wrong direction."

"Truer words were never spoken." His voice was ragged. "Why do women never know when it's time to talk and when it isn't?"

She stared at him, resentment making it easier to ignore her clamoring senses. "I thought you were above that kind of sexist remark."

"Lady, this is a hell of a time for a lecture on social attitudes. But go on, I'm all ears. You've wiped out the mood anyway."

Sitting up, Kim suddenly wished she hadn't been so

strong-minded. She buttoned her blouse with shaking fingers. "You remember we said neither of us would stake any claim on the other. That's why I'd better go work somewhere else."

"Really? And where would that be?" His features sharpened. "You're not thinking of working for that semiliterate sheet Warren publishes, are you?"

"Warren?" She realized she had actually forgotten the existence of Clint Warren. She laughed shakily. "Of course not. But I thought perhaps I should do what you suggested once before—apply for a job on the *Post*."

Swinging over the edge of the bed, he stood up and crossed to the window. "If you want to go to the *Post*, that's up to you. Just understand one thing: I never intended to alter the structure of your life. If you leave the *Recorder*, don't start thinking I forced you."

He was telling her that he didn't want to be involved.

"Jon, look." Kim swallowed the lumpiness in her throat. "This convention hasn't been exactly comfortable for either of us."

"So? I didn't want you here in the first place. You know that."

She stared at his remote back. "I . . . I didn't realize how it would be. I keep finding myself acting like someone else, someone I don't like. And even at the office, having to pretend you're a stranger . . . it's all so phony and unnatural."

"I suppose if I were truly gallant, I could settle the whole problem by making our association legal."

His tone made a joke of the words and Kim forced a laugh, but the drumming in her chest was almost unbearable. "I never said I expected anything like that."

"No, you wouldn't." His voice had a hard ring. "You're as freewheeling as I am, fortunately."

Silence made an island between them. Then Kim said hesitantly, "There's another solution."

"What's that?" He turned to face her.

"I could go on the night shift. That way we wouldn't see much of each other. You'd be going home at about the time I'd be reporting for work."

"The night shift." Putting his hands in his pockets, he took a few considering steps. "Well, it's an idea. . . ."

Disappointment stabbed her. Why did he have to be so instantly agreeable? "I'd work four to midnight," she said tentatively.

"Yes. Well, it might be the answer."

She bit down the tremor in her lower lip. Looking at his aloof face, she was reminded of Clint's harsh assessment of him.

"Thank you," she said woodenly.

"We try our utmost to oblige . . . given the opportunity." He moved to the door. "And now, after this thoroughly uninspired evening—"

"You haven't read the interview."

He wheeled, hiking an eyebrow. "You mean there's yet another fillip to this enchanting encounter?"

Kim kept her expression calm. Conscious of the unsettled feeling in her own body, she reminded herself that his sarcasm was engendered by erotic frustration. She crossed to the escritoire, plucked up her story and impulsively reached for her notebook too. "Jon, see this man?" She held up her sketch of the man who had been with Rachel on the plane. "Does he look familiar to you?"

Jon strode toward her. He held the notebook under

the lamplight for a long moment. "Mmm . . . those eyes . . ." He let out a whistle. "Where did you run into this weirdo?"

"On the plane. He was with Rachel. I had the feeling I'd seen him somewhere before."

His eyes had a shiny look. "No doubt you have. With Rachel, you say?"

She nodded.

"Maybe there's something to that old sawbone about woman's intuition. You said all along you didn't trust Rachel." He shook his head. "Hell of a note if the *Recorder* found itself promoting anyone with ties to this character."

"But who *is* he?"

He stared at the drawing. "This, my dear Miss Curtis, is either Jarvis Biggs or his double. Those crazy eyes . . . you got the guy down pat. He's the best hatemonger in the state." He shook his head as if to clear it. "I want to put in a call to Wally."

He walked around her, sank on the bed, picked up the phone. In a few minutes he was connected with the *Recorder*. "Get a reporter to check this out," he told Wally. "I want to find out if Biggs has any connection with the *Allenby Provider*. Get back to me soonest—I got the tip from a very reliable source."

Kim stood watching him. A reliable source. It was precisely what she felt like at the moment.

Her eyes traced the line of Jon's powerful shoulders, moved to the strong, long-fingered hands on the phone. Do I have any real meaning for this man? she wondered. Already he seemed to have completely forgotten that just a minute ago he was lying beside her on that bed.

But of course men did that, compartmentalized so readily. And to a newsman the story always came first. She had once seen a reporter staunching a terrible head wound with his notebook while phoning in a story about a street riot.

Jon put down the phone and stood up. "I won't look at your story now. If Biggs is behind that grass-roots party Rachel is promoting, we'll be doing an exposé of her instead of a feature." He gave a flicker of a smile. "Sharp work, Kim."

He left her with this miniscule compliment, and without a backward look. As the door closed, she suddenly realized that the night shift would leave her free only two evenings a week. Two instead of seven.

Surely he was aware of that, aware of how rarely she'd be able to see him! She felt her cheeks burning. If he'd been hoping to ease off the relationship, free himself for other things, she'd handed him the perfect out.

By so readily accepting her switch to the night shift, had Jon been telling her, in a subtle way, that he now found their romance more of an inconvenience than a joy?

Kim shivered, and suddenly felt she would never be warm again.

Chapter Twelve

She moved like a puppet on broken strings through the final day of the convention. On the night of the closing banquet, she dressed carefully, but her delphinium blue one-shoulder gown gave her as little pleasure as Jon's compliments, which to her ears had a stiff, manufactured sound.

When he made his address, which, from the opening sentence was plainly the high point of the convention, she took careful notes, smiled congratulations at him. That was the only time she had with him; although he had asked her to dance, the chairman grabbed his arm and spirited him off before they could get anywhere near the dance floor. He was still posing with the newly elected officers when the final notes of "Good Night, Ladies" filled the ballroom.

Kim went outside to wait for the elevator. A thin

little blonde in a puffy black taffeta gown stood in a corner with her bearded companion. They had their arms wrapped around each other's waists. "Who loves you?" the man whispered, nuzzling at the blonde's throat.

The words drummed in Kim's consciousness.

He's never said it, she thought, not once. He's shunned the word love as if it were lethal.

Yes, it was quite obvious Jon didn't return her intensity. To him their association was a dalliance, an airy thing, an arabesque. And she had to prepare herself for what was bound to eventually happen: The day he would lean across a restaurant table and say, Kim, something I have to tell you. The real thing's hit me. I'm in love, I'm going to marry so and so . . . Amy . . . somebody. . . .

Kim closed her eyes, oblivious to the voices around her, people saying goodbyes, talking about tomorrow morning's flight to Phoenix, Orlando, Boston. . . .

"Glad we don't have to make the wild rush to the airport in the dawn's early light."

She turned, saw Jon's flushed, triumphant face. He had been the hit of the convention, and in spite of everything, she couldn't help feeling a sudden swell of pride.

And then his words caught up with her, and she looked puzzledly at him.

"We'll have ourselves a nice, leisurely breakfast," he said. "Napa Valley's just an hour's drive. In this weather, it'll be glorious."

"Napa . . . ?"

"My brother's place, you remember. I've rented us a car."

"But . . . I've got a plane reservation. You never said you wanted me to come."

"Well, I'm asking you now. The kids are dying to meet our Lois Lane. Of course they're already convinced I'm Superman."

She looked up into the brilliance of his smile. "Well, that sounds . . ." All at once, as his shoulder touched hers, she felt a renewed awareness of how much he appealed to her. "Well, Jon," she said, "that sounds lovely, just lovely."

And it was. As their car wound up and down roads lined with lush vineyards, it was hard to believe that back home the grey dreariness of November was taking over. "I wish you could be here in early September, when the grapes are being pressed," Jon said. "The smell drives you crazy."

He insisted on stopping off to show her one of the famous wineries. They saw the wine flowing from pipes to be blended and casked, and they visited the sampling tables, sipping six different reds and whites. And as they drove off, the wine was working its magic, leaving them beamingly exuberant and very relaxed.

"Hey, why are you over there, ten thousand miles away?" Jon threw out an arm, pulling her to him, and Kim closed her eyes and felt the sun smiling down at them. All she could think was, Make this day last forever, make it never stop.

His arm was still around her when they pulled up at his brother's modest ranch house. For once Kim was able to keep all her problems at bay and live just for the moment. The bubble would burst soon enough, but right now it was shot through with the most exquisite colors and had the most delicate, nacreous sheen.

Jon's brother George was almost a replica of his father, a narrow-chested, pale man who smiled sweetly and spoke hardly at all. He was a physics professor at Berkeley. His wife was robust, apple-cheeked and talked constantly. Jenny Dumont was like a Fourth of July sparkler.

The four tow-headed boys fell upon their presents like ants on a chocolate bar.

"How did you do that, select just the right things for them?" Jenny called from the kitchen.

Kim was putting paper napkins on the dinner table. "I can't take the credit. Jon told me what interested them."

Over the magnificent crown roast she was bringing to the table, Jenny eyed Kim intently. "It's time Jon had children of his own to shop for. I told him he'll end up a lonely old man, but he claims he's ecstatically happy in his bachelorhood."

"He obviously is." Kim gave a carefully indifferent shrug.

"He's never brought a woman here before, so I thought maybe . . ."

"I'm about as interested in marriage as he is," Kim said.

At dinner she found herself looking at Jenny's children with more than casual attention, aware of a kind of beauty in the four freckled faces circling the table.

She particularly noted Jon's attitude toward them. Unlike some men she had known, he didn't seem afraid to speak in a gentle voice, didn't seem to feel that warm involvement with the children would hurt his masculine image. As he inclined his head toward the youngest child, she caught the family resemblance, and felt someday that Brucie's slim features would take on the rugged look of his uncle's.

Emotion welled up in her. She saw herself holding a child. In the background a man was looking over her shoulder, reaching to touch the child's tiny finger.

George was shyly suggesting a toast. "To our beautiful Lois Lane."

Jon raised his wine glass in Kim's direction. "She *is* beautiful, isn't she?"

And Kim, meeting his gaze, threw all caution to the winds. Once again she allowed the gates of her heart to open wide and embrace the vivid, enthralling flame of hope.

They came back to Philadelphia to find a fierce wind screaming up from the Delaware River. Even the stars looked frozen.

Home in her apartment, Kim felt the sag in energy that always followed a long jet flight. Tired but happy— the old cliché made her smile. When the phone rang, she lifted it dreamily.

And then she was sitting up, energized as always by his voice. "Didn't I just say goodbye to you, Mr. Dumont?" She laughed.

"I hate like the devil to do this to you," Jon said, "but it seems you're one on-the-ball reporter. Turns out there *is* a link between Rachel Moran and Jarvis Biggs; he's the candidate her grass-roots ticket intends to back. I'd like to hit the next edition on this. I'm heading to the office. You up to coming in?"

"Of course!"

Miraculously her weariness slipped away. She pulled on her grey flannel slacks, her white turtleneck. Pinning up her hair, she found herself smiling in the mirror. She had been right about Rachel Moran. And now she remembered where she had seen Jarvis Biggs—at Town Hall, at a meeting of some weird splinter group. This was a sizzling story. It would surely doom Rachel's phony political party.

She was yanking on her boots when a noise made her start and turn.

The living room door flew open.

She sat frozen, looking unbelievingly at the two men in the doorway.

Alan Skilton, holding his key.

And directly behind him, eyes hard, face glowering—*Jon.*

It was one of those weird coincidences that couldn't possibly have happened, but it had.

Somehow Kim lived through the awkward scene that followed. While her heart pounded indecently, she accepted the return of her key from Alan, who was leaving for Chicago the next day. She even managed to hold the door for him while he backed out, clutching the stereo to his chest. Jon then briefly explained what had happened. Apparently, he had seen only one cab at the cab stand and a man was just getting into it. "Where're you headed?" Jon called to the driver.

"Society Hill."

"That's where I'm going." Jon looked back at the passenger. "Mind if I share your cab? It's an emergency."

"Hop in."

168

The two men chatted briefly, then laughed to discover they were bound for the same street.

Stepping out of the cab, they made yet another amusing discovery: They were headed for the same apartment house.

When they paused in front of the same door—Kim's —and Alan produced his key, Jon abruptly stopped laughing.

After he'd given this terse description, Jon said shortly, "I'll phone for another cab." On their way to the office he sat looking straight ahead, motionless, remote as the pinpoint stars in the cold night sky.

Seeing the hard lines of his mouth, Kim felt an impulse to cry: Look, Alan and I have been over for a long time, and it wasn't anything much to begin with.

But why *should* she have to apologize? Would Jon explain *his* past emotional connections?

"Sorry I messed up your plans." Jon's voice was hard as the rap of a gavel.

"You didn't mess up any plans. I didn't know Alan was coming. I mean, I knew he planned to pick up his stereo sometime, but—"

"But since he had a key, he could come any time, right? That's why you really didn't want to go to Napa Valley—you were afraid you'd miss him."

"That isn't true!" In the passing street light she saw his hostile eyes and misery flooded her. How unfair he was, making her feel awkward and guilty for no reason!

"Yes, Alan had a key!" She slammed the words out. "In case he wanted to pick up his stereo when I was at work! And if I'd wanted a key to his place to borrow a . . . a book or something, he'd have given it to me! He trusted me! In fact, he wanted to marry me. And if you expect me to apologize for that, you're no one I want to know!"

The cab screeched to the curb. The *Recorder*'s white neon sign stained the pavement.

"Forget it." Jon opened the door. "We've got important things to think about."

The words speared her, gave her a sudden wild wish to return the pain. "That remark doesn't surprise me, Mr. Dumont! I've known all along how important I am to you—you've made it clear from the beginning!"

He didn't bother to turn his head.

"Crazy, putting somebody like you on the night shift," Pete Bailey said. "This place is going over the falls in a barrel. Now Dumont's zeroing in on expense accounts. I tell you, the morale around here is lower than a snake's waistline."

"I asked to be on the night shift, Pete," Kim said.

"We ought to get up a petition, haul the old man back from Europe," Pete went on bitterly.

Kim didn't answer, and as Pete drifted away she glanced in the direction of Jon's office. She knew he was in there—she'd seen his shadow behind the frosted glass.

His shadow was all she *had* seen since last Friday, when she'd completed the story on Rachel Moran's doomed political party. What was Jon thinking and feeling all this time? Did he have any idea how much tension there was in the newsroom? It grew more pronounced every day. He was alienating everyone, sending out caustic memos about expenses, demanding "more life, more color" in everybody's stories. She herself had felt a little hurt that he'd never even given her a thank-you for her hours of work on the Moran exposé.

But she knew Alan was the obvious reason behind his behavior to her. And she also knew she would never bring herself to do what Jon apparently expected—bow her head and contritely affirm she was heartily sorry she had ever had even the vaguest connection with another man.

Plucking up her coat, she headed dispiritedly out to the reception room. Cookie wasn't there. In fact, she realized, she hadn't seen Cookie for quite a while.

Disappointment crept over her. She had been hoping they could have dinner together. Cookie was a soothing influence, like an older sister, and at the moment Kim needed that kind of homely, feminine support.

"Miss Curtis?"

Two words.

Two words said by the only voice in the world that mattered.

She looked over her shoulder. He stood in the doorway of his office. "Spare a moment?" he said.

Wordlessly she walked in, carefully lowered herself in the chair opposite his desk. She watched as he walked to the window, standing with his back to her.

"Miss Curtis, I'd like to do a story on divorce. Have you read the latest figures in the Sunday edition?" He turned, thrust a clipping at her, his eyes avoiding hers.

She stared at the blurred jumble of type.

"Have you, Kim?"

"I vaguely remember reading them."

He still didn't meet her gaze. "I'd like you to work up an in-depth piece. Is the new sexual freedom the reason for the zooming divorce rate? Is it the institution of marriage that's outmoded? What's behind those figures?"

"All right."

"I have the feeling this is something you can do very well." For the first time his eyes almost touched her. "But then you do almost everything well."

She felt a small melting inside her, but she kept her face flat. If he was trying to say something, it wasn't enough, it wasn't half enough. This time he would have to dig down deep into himself—really give.

"I'll get right to work."

"Good. And if being on the night shift causes you any problems in getting interviews, you can switch back to day work." He paused. "That is, unless you'd like to change your mind completely, forget the night shift."

"No," she said quietly. "We decided."

"Well, then . . ." His shoulders swerved.

She'd been dismissed. She stood up, walked past the grey suit she remembered so well. Once she'd smudged lipstick near the left lapel. She saw the smudge was gone; he'd had it cleaned away, wiped out. Mechanically she put one foot before the other, and reached for the doorknob.

She heard the rushing movement before she realized what was happening. His large body lunged past her with the force of an avalanche, his arm went out. . . .

With an explosive sound of anger and pain, he slammed the door shut and stood against it, arms folded, his body a staunch barricade.

"Damn you." His eyes burned hers, seemed to devour her. "Come here. Come here to me."

Chapter Thirteen

"Have I told you your legs are unbeatable?" Jon said. "I know, I've studied thousands."

"I'm sure you have." Kim laughed. She felt as if she could never be grim again. Since that moment in the office when he had pulled her to him, asked her to meet him at his apartment, admitted that he needed her. . . .

He needed her. It was what she had been waiting to hear all along.

She felt his fingers touching her hair, playing with it. "You know what your friend Alan Skilton told me during that unforgettable taxi ride of ours?" he said lightly. "He said he was going to Chicago because a girl had driven him wild. Hard to believe you're such a heartless wench. I keep telling myself to watch my step with you."

Kim sensed the questions behind the comment and

decided she would tell him everything, just the way it had happened. This was a time to be completely open. "I'm afraid Alan dramatized quite a bit; nothing drives Alan wild unless it's the latest model automobile. Our engagement lasted less than a month."

"He seemed to think you were afraid of love because your parents had an unhappy marriage. You never told me that."

"You never asked. Anyway, they weren't actually unhappy. I just had the feeling there wasn't much passion. But that had nothing to do with why I wouldn't marry Alan. I simply didn't love him. Besides, *your* folks are happy, but you aren't exactly pining for a permanent alliance."

"Maybe I haven't found the right woman, someone docile enough." His eyes teased her. "Come over here—you're three inches too far away."

"And be docile for you? Not on your life!" But she let him pull her to him, relaxing as his lips moved on her throat.

"You're the color of honey," he whispered, "and you taste like honey."

She shivered and closed her eyes. "Oh, Jon," she cried impetuously, "how do people ever get to know what another person is about, what the other person needs and you need?"

"What *I* need is honey. More and more honey." His lips roamed over her skin. "Listen, you're on the late shift. Stay the night. You won't have to get up early."

"But *you* will! You said you're leaving for Washington, and you'll be gone all week."

He swore softly. "That's right, have to make the 6:09 train. But still, that leaves us seven hours. . . ."

Kim looked steadily at him. "I wouldn't want it that way, Jon. If I stayed, it . . . it shouldn't be hurried. I feel that strongly."

He studied her face. "You know what? All my barbaric instincts tell me to argue the point. But I have to agree with you—you can't make love on a timetable. It ought to be the most unhurried thing in the world." He touched the tip of her nose. "And so it will be, when I get back."

Impulsively Kim said, "I like you better right now than ever before, barbaric urges and all. In fact, I might have some barbaric urges of my own."

"I'm counting on that."

As she got into her storm coat, Jon put his favorite record back on the turntable. It was a golden oldie and its lyrics seemed to hold some special charm for him:

Some others I've seen might never be mean, might never be cross or try to be boss, but they wouldn't do. . . .

I'm not mean or cross, Kim thought. I don't try to be boss. But I'm *not* docile.

Maybe I haven't found someone docile enough, he'd said.

Just joking, of course. They had reached a new level of understanding, she told herself. Jon was getting to know more than the surface of her. At last they were growing to trust and respect each other.

"Have to talk to you." Pete Bailey grabbed Kim as she entered the newsroom. Being on the late shift gave her an odd feeling. There was only a skeleton staff, voices echoed with a strange hollowness and she couldn't get used to a different editor. She missed Wally.

"Listen, you know how lousy morale is around here," Pete said. "Well, today it's completely wiped out. We've drawn up a committee, and we want you to be our representative. We want you to go see Cookie."

"Cookie? What's up with Cookie?"

"She's been dumped. Dumont's fired her."

"Oh, come on. Mr. Dumont would never—"

"Oh, no? Haven't you run into the new streamlined secretary at Cookie's desk? And don't you recall two birds named Thornton and Halsey?"

"He would never fire Cookie," Kim said firmly, but she dimly remembered Clint Warren's prophesy: Dumont will be making a wholesale sweep of personnel. And Jon's own declaration: If it's a matter of survival, I'll fire anyone.

"Look," Pete said, "if management can get away with firing on the basis of age, we're all in trouble. We'll have to hire a lawyer, sue Dumont for unfair employment practices. But first we want to get the straight dope from Cookie. You're her friend, you're closest to her."

"I'll go ask Mr. Dumont, as soon as he gets back from Washington."

"Uh-uh. We're not waiting a minute on this. Look, Cookie's plants are gone, the picture of her husband's gone—what more proof do you need?" His eyes narrowed slyly. "Or maybe you're too pro-Dumont to handle the job."

"What does that mean?" Kim said sharply.

"Well, somebody spotted you in a cab with him. You two looked kind of cosy."

"I've ridden in cabs with you too, Bailey, but don't go reading anything into it!"

"Okay, okay, don't blow your stack. Will you represent the committee and talk to Cookie or won't you?"

"She could be on vacation," Kim offered limply, feeling as if she were defending a fallen flag. Oh, Jon, how could you? she thought.

And then abruptly she felt a wash of shame. Cookie was the person she should be thinking about. Maybe the woman was in trouble, needed a friend to lean on. . . .

"I'll see her first thing tomorrow," she told Pete decisively.

The neighbor who answered Cookie's phone was being neighborly, tending Cookie's plants. Cookie was in North Philadelphia General Hospital, the neighbor said. "But I really shouldn't tell you—she doesn't want any fuss."

And now Kim stood at the hospital entrance, her breath making frosty tunnels. She reached for the door, then paused, feeling a sudden streaking fear, a reluctance to go in.

Because she didn't want to be disappointed in Jon. It would simply shatter her heart.

"I just kept thinking I had something terrible," Cookie said. She looked lively, almost sparkly, tackling a huge lunch tray. "That was when I started taking days off from work. Then people began to phone me—Wally Forbes called four times—and I got the idea everyone at the office knew I had some horrible disease. I felt so ashamed!"

"Ashamed? You shouldn't feel ashamed of being sick!"

"Dear, women of my generation felt ashamed of everything, even if our slips were hanging. Anyway, I got this idea I'd made myself sick by working too hard—Mr. Dumont works such long hours—so I just up and quit."

"Quit? But I thought . . . everyone thought you were fired."

"Oh, no, I quit. Except that Mr. Dumont wouldn't let me. He made me take a leave of absence—with pay." Cookie smiled her Halloween smile. "You know, I didn't like him at first. He was so busy, he never stopped to chat. . . . But he's really a dear. See those African violets? They're Optimaras; he wired them from Washington. And he stuck to his promise. He didn't tell anyone I was having an operation. You didn't know, did you?"

"No, I didn't."

"I made him swear not to tell anyone. Let them think what they want, I said, I won't have them pitying me." Cookie laughed. "And now there's nothing to pity! I'm all better, and Mr. Dumont said on the phone this morning I can come back to work whenever I want."

"Mr. Dumont? Is he back in town?"

"Oh, yes, he got back this morning. He called me first thing. Goodness, that man had better watch out— I'll be setting my cap for him if he keeps courting me with flowers and things!"

Kim smiled shakily and stood up, joy and relief coursing through her as she said goodbye and moved to the door.

Chapter Fourteen

A few hours later, walking through the *Recorder* lobby, Kim saw Wally, coming off the day shift. She was startled when he passed her without even his usual sour smile.

"What's the matter?" she called playfully. "Have we stopped being friends now that I'm not on your shift?"

The city editor regarded her with flat eyes. "Miss Curtis, I've been with this paper twenty-six years. It's damned important to me, and I don't like people who don't value it."

"Don't value . . . ?" Kim's smile faded.

Without another glance in her direction, Wally hunched out the door. By the time she had recovered from her shock, he was a distant shape, half-obscured by swirling snow.

Feeling a vast, puzzled hurt, Kim plunged across the street to the Pressman's Bar. It was where she would be most likely to find Pete Bailey eating his dinner.

He was in the booth nearest the door. Kim slid in beside him. "I saw Cookie," she said without prelude. "And maybe now you people won't jump to conclusions so quickly. For your information, she's had a minor operation and Mr. Dumont gave her leave of absence. With pay, I might add. And that's all there is to that!"

"Well," Pete mumbled abashedly, "you have to stay on your feet around a guy like Dumont."

Kim brushed the words aside. "Pete—something funny just happened." She described her encounter with Wally.

"Yeah, I've been getting the same treatment. It's because we formed the committee about Cookie; somebody's spread the word we were talking down Dumont. I hear he's got wind of it, too. He thinks you and I are disloyal subjects, out to topple the throne."

"But that's ridiculous! I was the one who defended him!" Kim felt her heart racing. Was this the reason Jon hadn't phoned her now that he was back? "I won't stand for it! I won't have people saying things like that about me!"

"Come on, kid, have a beer. Let the boss man think anything he wants."

"No!" Kim jumped up. Her face felt on fire.

"Hey—where you going?"

She didn't answer. She ran to the door, stumbled through the snow and flagged an approaching cab.

She had to fix it right away, had to explain! She couldn't have Jon thinking she had acted sneakily, was disloyal to him and the paper. She had to make it plain Pete's committee wasn't her doing, that she'd never supported the talk about suing the management.

The cab was so old, she could hear its skeleton rattling. It took forever to heave up Broad Street, creak onto Walnut, but at last she saw the glimmer of the star-shaped light atop Walnut Towers. A sudden wetness stung her eyes. Did Jon really doubt her, believe she would talk him down to his employees?

You doubted him, she reminded herself, remembering the faint uncertainty she had felt right up to the moment she saw Cookie.

She plunged through the lobby, shot into the elevator and was noiselessly wafted to the penthouse. In a trance she crossed the carpet and lifted Jon's heavy brass lion's head knocker.

"I've *so* enjoyed seeing you again, Jon—"

The woman's voice was high, slightly affected. As Jon opened the door to Kim's knock, she saw a tall striking brunette in a long mink coat standing beside him.

"Oh!" Kim choked in a bog of humiliation. "I'm sorry!"

Jon's eyes were flat, resting on her. "Miss Schuman, this is Miss Curtis." He turned back to the woman in mink, smiled at her. "It's been nice, Connie."

"Always is, Jon!" The woman gave Kim a curious look and then went out the door in a swirl of mink.

Jon made an ironic, bowing movement at Kim. "Come in—can't have you standing out in the hall like a stranger."

Her throat suddenly felt raw. "I won't keep you long." Somehow she managed to keep her voice on a

181

straight path. "I just want to say"—she lifted her chin—"there's a report going around that I've been complaining about you, stirring up people at the office."

"Someone did call me with a disclosure to that effect."

"And you *believed* it?" She stared at him. "You don't hold me in very high esteem, do you? Not that you're obliged to. I never want you to feel any obligation!"

"Yes, obligation implies closeness, doesn't it, Kim? And I know closeness doesn't interest you, not real closeness. My sister-in-law Jenny told me you announced you had no interest in any involvement with me."

"That's not the way it was at all!" Kim cried. "Jenny said you were determined to stay—this is a direct quote—'an ecstatic bachelor.' She made quite a point of it. I assumed you used her to subtly pass the word along."

"Untrue!" He strode past her to the bar. He poured a drink so quickly it splashed across his sleeve. "Can I offer you one?"

"No, no . . ."

He turned, his eyes raking her face. "I would never bring up the subject of marriage in reference to you. You've made it plain you're not interested."

"And I suppose you are?" Kim laughed crookedly. "Why, you couldn't even accept a gift from me with grace! That cap—you acted as if I were putting steel shackles on you."

He was silent for a moment, then gave a quick nod. "That's true. I did feel threatened."

"Well, now you can relax!" Kim heard the quaver

threading in her voice despite the flip words. "I'm not threatening you. I never will."

"Won't you?" His voice was oddly muffled.

"It's funny," Kim went on. "I was the one who defended you about Cookie. I couldn't believe anything bad about you, and I thought you felt the same, thought you'd begun to value me. Now I see you actually look for things in me to criticize!"

"That isn't so." He stared into his untouched drink.

"Oh, yes, it is, and I know why! You hate my independence! You claim you want women to be full persons, but you don't live up to your editorials. Remember once you said you wanted someone docile? Well, that was the truth. You want someone who'll be a shadow!"

"You really believe that?" Slapping his glass down, he put his hands on her shoulders and stood looking down into her eyes, plunging into them. Kim cried, *"Oh!"* and twisted her head away. Seeing his face so close was like being wounded.

"Listen, you crazy, totally absorbing female, do you really believe I want you weak and mewling? You make it hell to deal with you, but it's your strength, your determined, lovely individuality that's caught me in a net. You're the kind of woman who makes life a twenty-four-hour adventure. I've sensed it from the beginning, but I didn't want to give in to it—no man does. I kept flipping over, trying to get out of your golden net, but everything kept pulling me back. Everything you ever said or did keeps playing in my mind, and now I know I'll be miserable all my life without you!"

Kim heard his words but couldn't absorb them,

couldn't believe what her eyes so plainly saw—the look of truth, the unhappiness in his face. Could all that really have something to do with her?

"You believed I plotted against you!" she gasped.

"No." He touched her mouth with a fingertip. "Not for a single minute. I told my informant I trusted you absolutely. You see, I believed we'd made a pledge with our eyes last week when you were here. I know I did."

"But . . . you just had a woman here!" She had a sense of flailing out, trying to save herself from the mesmerizing words she thought she had heard.

"A woman? Oh, you mean Connie?" His hold on her shoulders tightened. "Idiot. Connie's my decorator. She was supposed to make some changes around here, only I told her I couldn't go ahead as we originally planned . . . I was hoping I might possibly have a wife to help select things." His face came close to hers. "I was thinking of you, Kim. I love you—you've made me want to be a married man! There. I suppose you'll find it laughable."

"Laughable!" The joy filling Kim's throat bordered on pain. "Oh, Jon, I love you, I love you so much!"

His eyes widened. "Say that again." His body's warmth wrapped itself around her. "Say it again. By the tenth time maybe I'll believe it."

"I love you, Jon." Her voice was muffled against his chest, yet the words seemed to sing. And then a thought made her knit her eyebrows and she gazed up at him. "But, Jon, we're different from other people, we both need to feel free. Suppose we fight, grow horrible to each other and spoil things?"

He smiled a gentle, cherishing smile. "We're not that

different from everybody else, my lady of the fascinating eyes. I suspect in lots of ways we fit the everyday pattern—afraid we'll lose each other . . . prickly with jealousy." He shook his head. "Look at the outlandish thing I did at the convention—tipped a waiter to switch Clint Warren to another table, just to get him away from you. And then I fed myself a line that I was being protective, fatherly. . . ." His hands slid caressingly up her arms.

"Fatherly!" Kim laughed. "You really think you were ever fatherly?"

"People in love feed themselves all kinds of fantastic stories." His lips touched her hairline, and Kim swayed even closer to him, her body a flower expanding under the sun's embrace. "I suspect love makes us all a little crazy, so we give center stage to the dumb things . . . doubts, suspicions. Unless we're mature enough to realize the spotlight should be on what really counts— the way we feel about each other."

"We can try to remember that," Kim whispered, "can't we?"

"We'd be insane not to. We have what everyone in the world wants and not many even come close to."

"Oh, Jon, that's true, that's the big thing, isn't it?" She felt the sheen of tears in her eyes.

And then her attention was caught by a distant sound that drowned out the clamor of her heart. Chimes, ringing out the hour. "Jon! The office! I'm due back— I've got three hours left to my shift."

He smiled down at her. "No."

"Yes! I'd never run out on the paper—I couldn't!"

"My stubborn darling, I promise to honor your principles whenever feasible, but at this moment I will brook no argument." His lips swooped down, briefly flirted with the corner of her mouth. "Besides, it's a waste, you working on the night shift. I've got something better for you to do with your nights, something that will make superb use of your unusual talents."

Kim stared up at him. Then, catching his meaning, she felt a wave of heat in her face. Abruptly she realized that even in a modern woman's life there would always be some things it was permissible to feel shy about.

"Do you really think I'm that . . . talented, Mr. Dumont?" she said.

"Suppose we go and investigate," he replied.

And then, never taking his eyes from her face, he led her around the coffee table and past the suede sofa and the glittering, snow-flecked windows. . . .

She saw the soft lamplight of the bedroom, a beacon leading to joy, and the billowing down coverlet, waiting at last to embrace her and her midnight lover.

Silhouette Romance

15-Day Free Trial Offer
6 Silhouette Romances

6 Silhouette Romances, free for 15 days! We'll send you 6 new Silhouette Romances to keep for 15 days, absolutely free! If you decide not to keep them, send them back to us. You pay nothing.

Free Home Delivery. But if you enjoy them as much as we think you will, keep them by paying the invoice enclosed with your free trial shipment. We'll pay all shipping and handling charges. You get the convenience of Home Delivery and we pay the postage and handling charge each month.

Don't miss a copy. The Silhouette Book Club is the way to make sure you'll be able to receive every new romance we publish before they're sold out. There is no minimum number of books to buy and you can cancel at any time.

This offer expires July 31, 1984

Silhouette Book Club, Dept. **SRSR7G**
120 Brighton Road, Clifton, NJ 07012

Please send me 6 Silhouette Romances to keep for 15 days, absolutely free. I understand I am not obligated to join the Silhouette Book Club unless I decide to keep them.

NAME_____

ADDRESS_____

CITY_____STATE_____ZIP_____

Silhouette Romance

IT'S YOUR OWN SPECIAL TIME
Contemporary romances for today's women.
Each month, six very special love stories will be yours
from SILHOUETTE.

$1.50 each

☐ 5 Goforth	☐ 28 Hampson	☐ 54 Beckman	☐ 83 Halston
☐ 6 Stanford	☐ 29 Wildman	☐ 55 LaDame	☐ 84 Vitek
☐ 7 Lewis	☐ 30 Dixon	☐ 56 Trent	☐ 85 John
☐ 8 Beckman	☐ 32 Michaels	☐ 57 John	☐ 86 Adams
☐ 9 Wilson	☐ 33 Vitek	☐ 58 Stanford	☐ 87 Michaels
☐ 10 Caine	☐ 34 John	☐ 59 Vernon	☐ 88 Stanford
☐ 11 Vernon	☐ 35 Stanford	☐ 60 Hill	☐ 89 James
☐ 17 John	☐ 38 Browning	☐ 61 Michaels	☐ 90 Major
☐ 19 Thornton	☐ 39 Sinclair	☐ 62 Halston	☐ 92 McKay
☐ 20 Fulford	☐ 46 Stanford	☐ 63 Brent	☐ 93 Browning
☐ 22 Stephens	☐ 47 Vitek	☐ 71 Ripy	☐ 94 Hampson
☐ 23 Edwards	☐ 48 Wildman	☐ 73 Browning	☐ 95 Wisdom
☐ 24 Healy	☐ 49 Wisdom	☐ 76 Hardy	☐ 96 Beckman
☐ 25 Stanford	☐ 50 Scott	☐ 78 Oliver	☐ 97 Clay
☐ 26 Hastings	☐ 52 Hampson	☐ 81 Roberts	☐ 98 St. George
☐ 27 Hampson	☐ 53 Browning	☐ 82 Dailey	☐ 99 Camp

$1.75 each

☐ 100 Stanford	☐ 114 Michaels	☐ 128 Hampson	☐ 143 Roberts
☐ 101 Hardy	☐ 115 John	☐ 129 Converse	☐ 144 Goforth
☐ 102 Hastings	☐ 116 Lindley	☐ 130 Hardy	☐ 145 Hope
☐ 103 Cork	☐ 117 Scott	☐ 131 Stanford	☐ 146 Michaels
☐ 104 Vitek	☐ 118 Dailey	☐ 132 Wisdom	☐ 147 Hampson
☐ 105 Eden	☐ 119 Hampson	☐ 133 Rowe	☐ 148 Cork
☐ 106 Dailey	☐ 120 Carroll	☐ 134 Charles	☐ 149 Saunders
☐ 107 Bright	☐ 121 Langan	☐ 135 Logan	☐ 150 Major
☐ 108 Hampson	☐ 122 Scofield	☐ 136 Hampson	☐ 151 Hampson
☐ 109 Vernon	☐ 123 Sinclair	☐ 137 Hunter	☐ 152 Halston
☐ 110 Trent	☐ 124 Beckman	☐ 138 Wilson	☐ 153 Dailey
☐ 111 South	☐ 125 Bright	☐ 139 Vitek	☐ 154 Beckman
☐ 112 Stanford	☐ 126 St. George	☐ 140 Erskine	☐ 155 Hampson
☐ 113 Browning	☐ 127 Roberts	☐ 142 Browning	☐ 156 Sawyer

Silhouette Romance

IT'S YOUR OWN SPECIAL TIME
Contemporary romances for today's women.
Each month, six very special love stories will be yours
from SILHOUETTE.

$1.75 each

☐ 157 Vitek	☐ 170 Ripy	☐ 183 Stanley	☐ 196 Hampson
☐ 158 Reynolds	☐ 171 Hill	☐ 184 Hardy	☐ 197 Summers
☐ 159 Tracy	☐ 172 Browning	☐ 185 Hampson	☐ 198 Hunter
☐ 160 Hampson	☐ 173 Camp	☐ 186 Howard	☐ 199 Roberts
☐ 161 Trent	☐ 174 Sinclair	☐ 187 Scott	☐ 200 Lloyd
☐ 162 Ashby	☐ 175 Jarrett	☐ 188 Cork	☐ 201 Starr
☐ 163 Roberts	☐ 176 Vitek	☐ 189 Stephens	☐ 202 Hampson
☐ 164 Browning	☐ 177 Dailey	☐ 190 Hampson	☐ 203 Browning
☐ 165 Young	☐ 178 Hampson	☐ 191 Browning	☐ 204 Carroll
☐ 166 Wisdom	☐ 179 Beckman	☐ 192 John	☐ 205 Maxam
☐ 167 Hunter	☐ 180 Roberts	☐ 193 Trent	☐ 206 Manning
☐ 168 Carr	☐ 181 Terrill	☐ 194 Barry	☐ 207 Windham
☐ 169 Scott	☐ 182 Clay	☐ 195 Dailey	

$1.95 each

☐ 208 Halston	☐ 218 Hunter	☐ 229 Thornton	☐ 232 Hampson
☐ 209 LaDame	☐ 219 Cork	☐ 230 Stevens	☐ 233 Vernon
☐ 210 Eden	☐ 220 Hampson	☐ 231 Dailey	☐ 234 Smith
☐ 211 Walters	☐ 221 Browning	☐ 224 Langan	☐ 235 James
☐ 212 Young	☐ 222 Carroll	☐ 225 St. George	☐ 236 Maxam
☐ 213 Dailey	☐ 223 Summers	☐ 226 Hampson	☐ 237 Wilson
☐ 214 Hampson	☐ 216 Saunders	☐ 227 Beckman	☐ 238 Cork
☐ 215 Roberts	☐ 217 Vitek	☐ 228 King	☐ 239 McKay

IT'S YOUR OWN SPECIAL TIME
Contemporary romances for today's women.
Each month, six very special love stories will be yours
from SILHOUETTE. Look for them wherever books are sold
or order now from the coupon below.

$1.95 each